DYNAMICS OF REAL FLUIDS

DYNAMICS OF REAL FLUIDS

By

E. G. RICHARDSON, B.A., Ph.D., D.Sc.

Reader in Physics, King's College, Newcastle-on-Tyne,
University of Durham

LONDON
EDWARD ARNOLD & CO.

PRINTED AND BOUND IN GREAT BRITAIN BY
WILLIAM CLOWES AND SONS LIMITED, LONDON AND BECCLES

CONTENTS

v

CONTENTS

PLATES

CHAPTER 1

THE CLASSICAL APPROACH

Hydrodynamics deals with the motion of fluids, hydrostatics with fluids at rest. Fluids are usually divided into gases and liquids, although a good deal of the theory of fluids is applicable to both. For our purposes, the chief distinctions to be made are in density and compressibility. From the smaller density and greater compressibility of a gas arises its ability to fill the volume of any vessel in which it may be placed, whereas a small quantity of liquid in a large vessel presents a free surface from which it may evaporate into the space above and at which forces—surface tensions—are apparent. At the "critical point" of a fluid these distinctions are confounded and the liquid becomes vapour without a sudden change in properties. Both types of fluid show resistance to motion in which a further property, viscosity, comes into play. If parts of the fluid are interconnected, elastic forces may operate when one part is moved relative to another, though this only occurs in liquids.

In the motion of fluids, then, the subject of this book, the physical properties of matter in the fluid state which will have to be considered are: density, compressibility in bulk, surface tension, viscosity, and shear elasticity.

The actual motion of portions of the fluid results from differences of pressure or of density. The fluid tends to run down a gradient of pressure and from a place where the fluid is compressed to one where it is rarefied until equilibrium is restored. Continuous movement ensues when unbalanced pressure differences are continually maintained by external forces.

The Ideal Fluid

Since it would be difficult to construct equations involving simultaneously all the factors we have just enumerated and the solution of them when constructed virtually impossible, the fluid is simplified in "classical theory" as follows:

1. The fluid retains the same density throughout.
2. The fluid is incompressible.

(These conditions are not synonymous, though they have the same effect. In the molecular picture of the processes of locally heating or of mechanically compressing a fluid, the former is supposed to increase the molecular kinetic energy, the latter to bring the particles closer together. A "hot spot" diffuses outwards, a compression travels out as a sound wave.)

1

3. The fluid is inelastic.

4. The fluid has no free surface.

These restrictions leave the fluid with mass (or inertia) and viscosity, but further simplification of the mathematics ensues if we suppose the fluid frictionless.

The Equations of Motion of the Ideal Fluid

The equations are constructed from the statement of Newton's Second Law of Motion, i.e. that the total force acting on a particle is the product of its mass and acceleration.

If x, y, z are the rectilinear co-ordinates of a small cube of the material

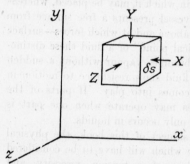

Fig. 1.   Forces on fluid element.

(density ρ) of volume δv, $\ddot{x}$, $\ddot{y}$, $\ddot{z}$ the components of its acceleration and X, Y, Z of force on unit mass, let X_p, Y_p, Z_p be the components of the *external* force acting normally on the three surfaces of area δS due to the differences of pressure (Fig. 1). Setting aside the frictional forces for the moment, we have these conditions of equilibrium:

$$\left.\begin{array}{l} \rho\ddot{x}\delta v = X\rho\delta v + X_p\delta S \\ \rho\ddot{y}\delta v = Y\rho\delta v + Y_p\delta S \\ \rho\ddot{z}\delta v = Z\rho\delta v + Z_p\delta S \end{array}\right\} \quad . \quad (1)$$

In place of X_p, Y_p, Z_p we shall insert the pressure gradients in the corresponding directions, i.e.

$$\left.\begin{array}{l} X_p . \delta S = \dfrac{\partial p}{\partial x} . \delta v \\[2mm] Y_p . \delta S = \dfrac{\partial p}{\partial y} . \delta v \\[2mm] Z_p . \delta S = \dfrac{\partial p}{\partial z} . \delta v \end{array}\right\} \quad . \quad . \quad . \quad . \quad (2)$$

For, in an ideal fluid, the pressure acts equally in all directions in the interior and at right angles to any surface presented to it. Then X_p, Y_p, Z_p are each derived from p, the mean hydrostatic pressure at the point in the fluid circumscribed by the cube.

Substituting in (1) we get

$$\left.\begin{array}{l} \rho\ddot{x} = \rho X - \dfrac{\partial p}{\partial x} \\[2mm] \rho\ddot{y} = \rho Y - \dfrac{\partial p}{\partial y} \\[2mm] \rho\ddot{z} = \rho Z - \dfrac{\partial p}{\partial z} \end{array}\right\} \quad . \quad . \quad . \quad (3)$$

These equations are not suited to direct application since the quantities x, y, z appear in them at once as dependent and independent variables. There are two ways of adapting them to suit experimental observation. We can ask ourselves, "At a given point, what fluid occupies the element of space subsequently?" or, "Where does a given particle find itself as time goes on?" The first attitude corresponds to that of a fixed observer, the second to that of an observer who moves with the general velocity of the medium.

Mathematically, the first question can be put thus: "What function of x, y, z, and t are the velocity components $U(=\dot{x})$, $V(=\dot{y})$, $W(=\dot{z})$?" We proceed to retain x, y, z as independent variables but eliminate their dependent aspects to obtain

$$\frac{d^2x}{dt^2}=\frac{dU}{dt}=\frac{\partial U}{\partial t}+\frac{\partial U}{\partial x}\cdot\frac{dx}{dt}+\frac{\partial U}{\partial y}\cdot\frac{dy}{dt}+\frac{\partial U}{\partial z}\cdot\frac{dz}{dt}, \text{ etc.*} \qquad . \quad . \quad (3a)$$

which with (3) resolve into the Eulerian† equations:

$$\left.\begin{array}{l}\dfrac{\partial U}{\partial t}+U\dfrac{\partial U}{\partial x}+V\dfrac{\partial U}{\partial y}+W\dfrac{\partial U}{\partial z}=X-\dfrac{1}{\rho}\cdot\dfrac{\partial p}{\partial x}\\[2mm]\dfrac{\partial V}{\partial t}+U\dfrac{\partial V}{\partial x}+V\dfrac{\partial V}{\partial y}+W\dfrac{\partial V}{\partial z}=Y-\dfrac{1}{\rho}\cdot\dfrac{\partial p}{\partial y}\\[2mm]\dfrac{\partial W}{\partial t}+U\dfrac{\partial W}{\partial x}+V\dfrac{\partial W}{\partial y}+W\dfrac{\partial W}{\partial z}=Z-\dfrac{1}{\rho}\cdot\dfrac{\partial p}{\partial z}\end{array}\right\} \quad . \quad . \quad . \quad (4)$$

Now let us introduce the frictional forces. We define the coefficient of viscosity, η, as the force per unit area of two parallel laminae of fluid unit distance apart, measured across the direction of flow. Thus, if U and $U+\delta U$ (Fig. 2) are the velocities (in the direction of x) at two planes δy apart, the force per unit area

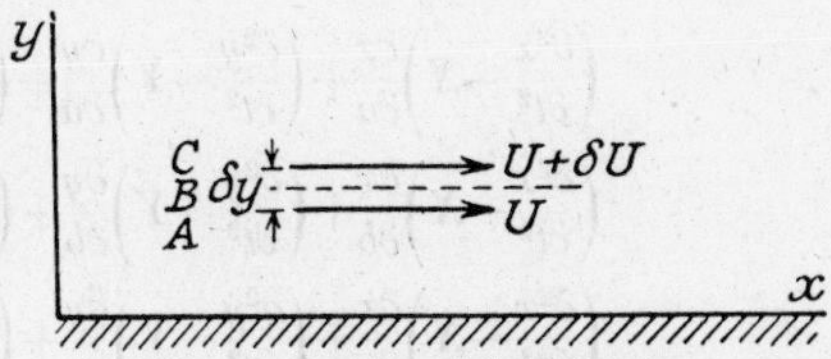

Fig. 2.   Action of fluid friction.

on the fluid in either plane is $\eta.\partial U/\partial y$, i.e. the product of the coefficient of viscosity and the velocity gradient perpendicular to the direction of flow. If A, B, and C are such laminae, each of area S, A exerts a force on B equal to $-\eta.\partial U/\partial y.S$; C exerts a force on B equal to $\eta(\partial U/\partial y+\partial^2 U/\partial y^2.\delta y)S$, so that the net force on B is

$$\eta\frac{\partial^2 U}{\partial y^2}.\delta yS=\frac{\eta}{\rho}.\delta m.\frac{\partial^2 U}{\partial y^2}=\eta.\delta v.\frac{\partial^2 U}{\partial y^2}$$

where δm is the mass of fluid between A and B. The factor η/ρ, written ν, which we shall often require, is called the kinematic (coefficient of)

* The rate of change in any property of the fluid such as U, written dU/dt, can be divided into a *local* change, $\partial U/\partial t$, which the property suffers when the place of observation remains fixed and the *convective* change, i.e. the remaining three terms, which U experiences as one alters the place of observation.

† *Acad. Berlin* (1755).

viscosity. (It should be noted that it is here assumed that η is constant for a given fluid, invariable with $\partial U/\partial y$, but later in the book we shall meet systems in which the two are interdependent.)

In the general case, the total viscous force on an element of mass m due to the component U will be

$$\eta\,\delta v\left(\frac{\partial^2 U}{\partial x^2}+\frac{\partial^2 U}{\partial y^2}+\frac{\partial^2 U}{\partial z^2}\right)$$

written shortly $\nu m \nabla^2 U$. This force must be added to those on the right-hand side of the equations we have already derived; in particular, (4) become

$$\left.\begin{aligned}
\frac{\partial U}{\partial t}&=X-\frac{1}{\rho}\frac{\partial p}{\partial x}+\nu\nabla^2 U \\
\frac{\partial V}{\partial t}&=Y-\frac{1}{\rho}\frac{\partial p}{\partial y}+\nu\nabla^2 V \\
\frac{\partial W}{\partial t}&=Z-\frac{1}{\rho}\frac{\partial p}{\partial z}+\nu\nabla^2 W
\end{aligned}\right\} \quad \ldots \ldots \quad (5)$$

equations ascribed to Navier[*] and Stokes.[†]

The second form of our question (*vide supra*) can be translated thus: "What functions of time and place are those co-ordinates—let them be a, b, c—which characterise a given particle?" To answer this, we get rid of x, y, z as independent variables but retain them where dependent and arrive at the Lagrangian[‡] form of the equations of motion:

$$\left.\begin{aligned}
\left(\frac{\partial^2 x}{\partial t^2}-X\right)\frac{\partial x}{\partial a}+\left(\frac{\partial^2 y}{\partial t^2}-Y\right)\frac{\partial y}{\partial a}+\left(\frac{\partial^2 z}{\partial t^2}-Z\right)\frac{\partial z}{\partial a}+\frac{1}{\rho}\frac{\partial p}{\partial a}&=0 \\
\left(\frac{\partial^2 x}{\partial t^2}-X\right)\frac{\partial x}{\partial b}+\left(\frac{\partial^2 y}{\partial t^2}-Y\right)\frac{\partial y}{\partial b}+\left(\frac{\partial^2 z}{\partial t^2}-Z\right)\frac{\partial z}{\partial b}+\frac{1}{\rho}\frac{\partial p}{\partial b}&=0 \\
\left(\frac{\partial^2 x}{\partial t^2}-X\right)\frac{\partial x}{\partial c}+\left(\frac{\partial^2 y}{\partial t^2}-Y\right)\frac{\partial y}{\partial c}+\left(\frac{\partial^2 z}{\partial t^2}-Z\right)\frac{\partial z}{\partial c}+\frac{1}{\rho}\frac{\partial p}{\partial c}&=0
\end{aligned}\right\} \quad . \quad (6)$$

The form due to Euler is, however, more generally used.

With the force equations, such as (5), we combine the equations of continuity which express that the quantity of fluid entering a volume element in a certain time must equal that which leaves it plus or minus any accumulation or reduction of mass in the space. In the Eulerian form,

$$\frac{d\rho}{dt}=\frac{\partial\rho}{\partial t}+\rho\left(\frac{\partial U}{\partial x}+\frac{\partial V}{\partial y}+\frac{\partial W}{\partial z}\right)=0$$

or, since we have supposed that ρ is constant,

$$\frac{\partial U}{\partial x}+\frac{\partial V}{\partial y}+\frac{\partial W}{\partial z}=0 \quad . \ldots \ldots \quad (7)$$

[*] *Mem. Acad. Sci.* (*Paris*) (1822).　　　　[†] *Camb. Trans.*, **8**, 287 (1845).
[‡] *Mem. Acad.* (*Berlin*) (1781).

To equations such as (5) and (7) must be added others characterising the conditions of the fluid at its boundaries (usually solid). These express, for instance, that the normal component of the velocity must vanish at a solid boundary, or be the same on each side of any point in the boundary between two fluids; and that the tangential component must vanish at the boundary formed by a stationary solid, or be continuous on each side of a fluid interface or free surface. The second of these conditions is sometimes expressed in the dictum: "no slip at the boundary." There results from it a gradient of velocity going outwards from the boundary into the mainstream and so a force on unit area of the boundary, made manifest as a drag or resistance offered by the boundary to the motion.

Nevertheless, the Navier–Stokes equations have up to the present defied solution in their complete form and other means have to be adopted for tackling the problem of resistance in a fluid having both inertia and viscosity.

Before describing these we shall consider two simplifications of the equations which lead to solutions whose application is strictly limited to ideal fluids but which have a limited application to special types of flow of real fluids.

These ideal types are:
    (1) fluids without viscosity, having only mass (or inertia),
    (2) fluids having negligible inertia, only viscosity.

Steady Potential Flow

If we omit the viscosity terms from equations (5) and also suppose that all velocities are steady, we are left with a fluid which can move in two ways, irrotational or rotational. The second boundary condition is no longer relevant, but the first still holds.

The *circulation* round a closed path from A back to A is defined as the integral round the path of the product of the velocity component along the path at any point and an element of the path at the same location, reckoned at any epoch of time:

$$\Gamma = \oint_A^A U ds$$

The simplest instance of circulation in a fluid is that of a vortex. If Ω is the angular velocity of the particles in the vortex and a track is described round the core of a radius r,

$$\Gamma = \int \Omega r^2 d\theta = 2\pi r^2 \Omega$$

Kelvin showed that in a frictionless fluid the circulation round a closed path remains constant for all time.

Stream tubes or lines represent imaginary canals in the fluid along which a particle started from one end moves continually to the other, as though so constrained like a train in a tunnel.

The line integral of the circulation over the path between two points is constant whatever the form of the path and is known as the *velocity potential*. The potential difference between two points A and B is $_A\phi_B=\int_A^B U.ds$. If we measure potential from an arbitrary "level" in the fluid we can call this a surface of zero potential and

$$\phi_A=\int_0^A U.ds; \quad \phi_B=\int_0^B U.ds; \quad \phi_B\phi-_A=\int_A^B U.ds$$

A plane which passes through all points in the field of flow having the same potential is called an equipotential surface. From the fact that the fluid when it moves takes the line of least resistance we may infer that the stream tubes cut the equipotential surfaces at right angles. (In the same way, a field of force, gravitational, magnetic, or electrical, may be delineated as a series of equipotential surfaces intersected by stream tubes. The contour map of a countryside is such a field represented in two dimensions where the lines of equal height are equipotential lines reckoned from sea-level as zero and the directions in which streams run are lines of force.)

A solid boundary itself forms one side of a stream tube or cylinder; since fluid cannot move across the boundary no tube can intersect it; and the equipotential surfaces terminate on the solid boundary as perpendiculars to it.

The difference of potential along a portion of a stream-line of length δs is $U\delta s$ or $U=d\phi/ds$. Thus the velocity is given by the gradient of the potential:

$$U=\text{grad. } \phi \quad\quad\quad . \quad . \quad . \quad . \quad . \quad . \quad (8)$$

From Kelvin's theorem it follows that a frictionless fluid started from rest cannot grow vortices or, if it is in motion with vortices in it, cannot rid itself of them. Such a fluid started from rest must have a potential field, but we do not by that imply that all the stream tubes must be straight. Curvature of the stream tubes *per se* does not set at naught the Kelvin theorem.

If we agree to describe our equipotential field so that each line is one step removed from the next and label them—in potential units—0, 1, 2, 3, etc., then wherever the tubes are constricted and crowded together, the velocity is higher than the mean; where they are wide and distended, on the contrary, the velocity must be below the average. Our definition of a stream tube and the condition of incompressibility in the fluid necessitate this. (The same thing is true of a field of force. Where the contour lines on a map are close together the terrain is steep and water runs off in this vicinity with a large acceleration. So, too, on a magnetic map the force of attraction or repulsion on a pole is large at a place where the lines of force are close together.)

Given a potential function ϕ we can resolve its gradients in the three directions x, y, z, and take

$$U=\frac{\partial\phi}{\partial x}; \quad V=\frac{\partial\phi}{\partial y}; \quad W=\frac{\partial\phi}{\partial z} \quad . \quad . \quad . \quad . \quad (9)$$

with the equation of continuity (7), to get:

$$\frac{\partial^2\phi}{\partial x^2}+\frac{\partial^2\phi}{\partial y^2}+\frac{\partial^2\phi}{\partial z^2}=0, \text{ written } \nabla^2\phi=0 \quad . \quad . \quad . \quad (10)$$

the so-called Laplace equation.

From equations (3a) we derive an important theorem, writing

$$\frac{dU}{dt}dx=\frac{\partial U}{\partial t}dx+U\left(\frac{\partial U}{\partial x}.dx+\frac{\partial U}{\partial y}dy+\frac{\partial U}{\partial z}.dz\right)$$

$$=\frac{\partial U}{\partial t}.dx+UdU, \text{ etc.}$$

so that, when at a certain place the pattern of flow is fixed, i.e. U, V, W are constant in time:

$$\frac{dU}{dt}.dx+\frac{dV}{dt}.dy+\frac{dW}{dt}.dz=UdU+VdV+WdW=d\left(\frac{U^2+V^2+W^2}{2}\right)$$

and

$$d\left(\frac{\partial\phi}{\partial t}\right)+d\left(\frac{U^2+V^2+W^2}{2}\right)=-dE-\frac{dp}{\rho}, \text{ by (4),}$$

where E is a potential for the inertia forces, such that

$$X=-\frac{\partial E}{\partial x}; \quad Y=-\frac{\partial E}{\partial y}; \quad Z=-\frac{\partial E}{\partial z}$$

When the flow is steady $\partial\phi/\partial t=0$ and the mean velocity is U. This gives us, on integration, D. Bernoulli's[*] theorem:

$$\frac{U^2}{2}+E+\frac{p}{\rho} \text{ is constant} \quad . \quad . \quad . \quad . \quad . \quad (11)$$

This applies with a distinguishing value for the constant along each and every tube of flow, but in the absence of vorticity the constant is the same for all tubes. In hydrodynamics E often characterises a mass of fluid lifted or lowered under gravity through a height h, and the theorem then becomes

$$\frac{U^2}{2}+gh+\frac{p}{\rho} \text{ is constant} \quad . \quad . \quad . \quad . \quad (11a)$$

When all the motion is on a horizontal plane, it simplifies still further to

$$\frac{U^2}{2}+\frac{p}{\rho} \text{ is constant} \quad . \quad . \quad . \quad . \quad (11b)$$

Applying (11b) to the tube which marches with a solid lamina placed in the field, the pressure exerted on the body is small when the tube is narrow and the speed high, and *vice versa*.

[*] *Hydrodynamica* (1788).

In place of the velocity potential or alongside it, we may employ, if we please, the stream function. If we join two points A and B by a curved segment of length ds, making an angle α with the stream velocity at that place, the stream function is so defined that

$$\psi_B - \psi_A = \int_A^B U \sin \alpha . ds$$

In moving along a stream tube from A to B, α remains zero or is constant along a stream tube. Otherwise, if U be resolved along the three co-ordinate axes into U, V, W, making with the normal to ds angles whose cosines (the "direction cosines") are l, m, n,

$$\psi = \int (lU + mV + nW) ds \quad . \quad . \quad . \quad . \quad (12)$$

If we take axes at each point on the tube directed along and perpendicular to the tangent and if r_1 is the radius of curvature and s a portion of the tube, the two components of acceleration are U^2/r_1 and $\partial U/\partial t$ or $U\partial U/\partial s$. We can then form equations on the model of (3):

$$\rho U \frac{\partial U}{\partial s} = \rho T - \frac{\partial p}{\partial s}$$

$$\frac{\rho U^2}{r_1} = \rho N - \frac{\partial p}{\partial r_1} \quad . \quad . \quad . \quad . \quad . \quad (12a)$$

where T and N represent the tangential and normal components of force on unit mass.

These are called the "intrinsic equations" and from them when a potential applies to T and N we can derive Bernoulli's theorem. For then

$$T = -\frac{\partial E}{\partial s}; \quad N = -\frac{\partial E}{\partial r_1}$$

and an integration of the first of the equations (12a) gives (11).

Examples of Potential Flow

We shall, for simplicity, take our examples from two-dimensional motion; that is, motion which takes place in a thin plane or in which the cross-sections of flow taken by a plane at various values of z are identical. A map of the field will then consist of a set of equipotential lines and streamlines. Since $d\psi$ is the total variation of a function of two independent variables. x and y,

$$d\psi = U dy - V dx = \frac{\partial \psi}{\partial x} . dx + \frac{\partial \psi}{\partial y} . dy$$

or
$$U = \frac{\partial \psi}{\partial y}; \quad V = -\frac{\partial \psi}{\partial x} \quad . \quad . \quad . \quad . \quad (13)$$

then with $U = \partial\phi/\partial x$ and $V = \partial\phi/\partial y$ (cf. (9)), we obtain the three equations:

$$\nabla^2\phi = 0; \quad \nabla^2\psi = 0; \quad \frac{\partial\phi}{\partial x} . \frac{\partial\psi}{\partial x} + \frac{\partial\phi}{\partial y} . \frac{\partial\psi}{\partial y} = 0 \quad . \quad . \quad . \quad (14)$$

(A) Point source or sink. Imagine liquid to well up from an underground spring through a hole on to a horizontal surface. The streamlines over the surface will be straight, radiating from the hole, and the equipotential lines concentric circles. In polar co-ordinates, $\psi = C\theta$; $-\partial\phi/\partial r = C/r$. (Interchange ψ and ϕ in these expressions and you have the whirlpool.) In hydrodynamical parlance this is a "source." Set $\partial\phi/\partial r = +C/r$ and you have the "sink," a hole into which the liquid drains from the plate. C is known as the strength of the source or sink.

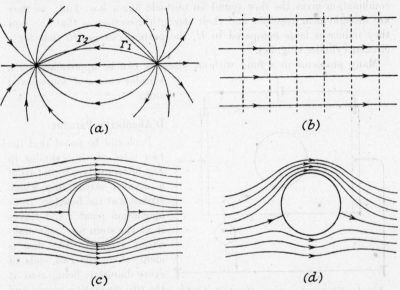

Fig. 3. Potential flow: (a) source and sink, (b) uniform stream, (c) stationary cylinder, (d) rotating cylinder in stream.

A source and sink of the same strength near together form a "dipole" and have a potential field,

$$\phi = C \log \frac{r_1}{r_2}$$

where this value applies to a point distant r_1 and r_2 from source and sink respectively (Fig. 3a).

(B) Parallel flow. Steady streaming of fluid in the direction of x with velocity U will have a field

$$\phi = Ux; \quad \psi = Uy$$

the two sets forming a pattern of checkers (Fig. 3b).

(C) Flow past a cylinder. The axis of the cylinder is the z co-ordinate and is placed in an erstwhile uniform stream U. We obtain a close approximation to the flow round the cylinder by superposing the systems

A and B, as a dipole plus a uniform streaming. Transformed into polar co-ordinates this becomes,

$$\phi = U\left(r + \frac{a^2}{r}\right) \cos \theta; \quad \psi = U\left(r - \frac{a^2}{r}\right) \sin \theta$$

i.e.
$$\phi = C \log \frac{r_1}{r_2} + Ux$$

If the source and sink are in line with the stream and fairly distant, the combination gives the flow round an obstacle like a boat hull; as they are brought near together and their strength increased so that the flow they induce is large compared to U, the pattern changes to that for a circular cylinder (Fig. 3c).

Many problems in a fluid without viscosity can be approached by a suitable choice of sources and sinks.

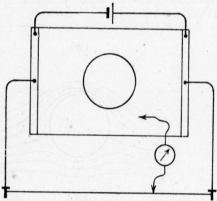

Fig. 4.   Electrical analogue of potential field.

D'Alembert's Paradox

It should be noted that the two sides of the cylinder in Fig. 3c themselves form part of a divided stream-line which strikes it at the bow (or "front stagnation point") and leaves it at the stern (or "rear stagnation point"). The flow is identical at the two ends of every diameter, being zero at the two stagnation points and a maximum at the ends of the equator. By Bernoulli's theorem, the forces inward at the two ends of each diameter cancel out in pairs, so that the cylinder experiences no net force or resistance. This consequence of the neglect of viscous forces was first pointed out by d'Alembert.

Magnus Effect

If the flow is, however, unsymmetrical with respect to the x axis we can simulate it by adding a circulation in the form of concentric stream lines to the patterns we have drawn already. Thus a clockwise circulation added to the pattern of the circular cylinder has the effect of increasing the general flow on the positive side of y and decreasing it on the negative side (Fig. 3d). This makes the pressure on the cylinder, due to the stream-line which bathes it, less above than that just below and the obstacle experiences a cross-force (Magnus* effect).

* *Abhand. Berlin. Akad. Sci.* (1851).

We have already remarked on the analogy between hydrodynamic fields of flow and magnetic or electrostatic fields of force. The equipotential lines in a two-dimensional electrostatic field may be mapped on a model field made in silver foil or in a shallow trough of acidulated water. This forms two arms of a Wheatstone bridge, the other pair, the ratio arms, being made of a uniform wire (Fig. 4). The fall of potential takes place through plane and wire in parallel and is provided by a battery. The galvanometer is connected at one end to a point on the wire, while a wander-plug at the other end is used to search for points in the field exhibiting the same potential as the connection to the wire, shown by absence of deflection of the galvanometer needle. Such places are joined by a line, the potential divider moved to a new place on the wire, and the process repeated. Boundaries to the field of flow or of force and obstacles in it are simulated by slips of ebonite of appropriate shape. Thus the field of Fig. 3c is exhibited in facsimile by the electric field over a metal foil between thick strips with a circular hole cut out of the foil.

Viscosity large compared with Inertia

If in equations (5) we neglect the inertia forces in comparison with the viscous ones and assume steady flow, we obtain equations in the form discussed by Stokes, i.e.

$$\left.\begin{array}{l} \dfrac{\partial p}{\partial x} = \eta \nabla^2 U \\[2mm] \dfrac{\partial p}{\partial y} = \eta \nabla^2 V \\[2mm] \dfrac{\partial p}{\partial z} = \eta \nabla^2 W \end{array}\right\} \quad \cdots \cdots \quad (15)$$

which in the two-dimensional case—last equation of (15) omitted—can be combined into a single derivative of a stream function, as

$$\nabla^4 \psi = 0$$

A simple example of such a flow can be envisaged where a very viscous liquid runs over a horizontal plate extending in the direction of the x axis in such a fashion that the velocity over a plane at any level is uniform but varies, due to viscosity, from plane to plane over the plate. Equations (15) then reduce to

$$\frac{\partial p}{\partial x} = \eta \frac{\partial^2 U}{\partial y^2} \quad \cdots \cdots \quad (15a)$$

Equations of this type occur in the theory of the lubrication of roller bearings.

Two other instances of this solely viscous flow to which we must refer later are (A) flow in a narrow tube; (B) flow between concentric rotating cylinders.

(A) The force due to the pressure gradient on a cylinder of liquid of radius r (measured from the axis) of a circular tube and δx in length is

$$\pi r^2 \frac{\partial p}{\partial x} \cdot \delta x$$

and the frictional force round its outer periphery is

$$-2\pi r \delta x \eta \frac{\partial U}{\partial r}$$

By equating these we get the velocity gradient across the direction of flow,

$$\frac{\partial U}{\partial r} = -\frac{r}{2\eta} \cdot \frac{\partial p}{\partial x} \quad \ldots \ldots \ldots \quad (16)$$

increasing from zero at the axis to a maximum at the wall of the tube. Integrating we find the velocity to be proportional to $a^2 - r^2$—on inserting the condition that it must vanish at the wall $r=a$—so that it increases in parabolic form to the centre of the tube. As Poiseuille* showed experimentally and as we may deduce by a second integration, the overall outflow from the tube per second is proportional to the fourth power of the radius,

$$Q = \frac{\pi}{2\eta} \cdot \frac{\partial p}{\partial x} \int_0^a (a^2 - r^2) r \, dr = \frac{\pi a^4}{8\eta} \cdot \frac{\partial p}{\partial x} \quad \ldots \ldots \quad (17)$$

(B) Consider an annulus of liquid δr thick at a radius r from the common axis of the two cylinders (of supposedly unit height). If the angular velocity of the inner periphery of the annulus is ω and that of the outer $\omega + \partial \omega / \partial r \cdot \delta r$, $\delta(\omega r)$ or $(\omega + r \cdot \partial \omega / \partial r) \delta r$ is the difference in peripheral velocity and the velocity gradient causing shear is $r \partial \omega / \partial r$.

The moment about the axis of the viscous force on the annulus is therefore $2\pi \eta r^3 \cdot \partial \omega / \partial r$ per unit length. The value of this, reckoned from a, the radius of the inner and usually stationary cylinder—being so retained against the twist of a spring or suspending thread—out to any radius r, is

$$M = 4\pi \eta \omega \frac{a^2 r^2}{r^2 - a^2} = 4\pi \eta \Omega \frac{a^2 b^2}{b^2 - a^2} \quad \ldots \ldots \quad (18)$$

when r is set equal to b, the radius of the outer (hollow) cylinder, rotated at a constant angular speed Ω.

After eliminating M from these equations to get ω at any radius r in terms of a, b, and Ω, we derive the velocity gradient in the form:

$$r \frac{\partial \omega}{\partial r} = 2\Omega \frac{1/r^2}{1/a^2 - 1/b^2} \quad \ldots \ldots \ldots \quad (19)$$

This type of flow was first studied by Couette.† A similar solution applies to Searle's‡ apparatus, in which the inner cylinder is rotated and the outer held still against the twist of its axis.

* *Comptes Rendus*, **11**, 12 (1840).   † *Ann. chim. phys.*, **21**, 433 (1890).
‡ *Proc. Camb. Phil. Soc.*, **16**, 600 (1912).

Plots of the velocity across the interspace are shown in a later figure (Fig. 77), and on p. 58 the stability of this type of motion is discussed.

Force on an Immersed Obstacle in a very Viscous Fluid

Using equations of the type (15), Stokes* worked out the stream tubes for the case of a sphere immersed in a viscous fluid, while neglecting the inertia, as

$$\psi = \tfrac{3}{4} U a \left(r - \frac{a^2}{3r} \right) \sin^2 \theta \quad \cdots \cdots \quad (20)$$

These differ from the corresponding ones for potential in inviscid flow in the vicinity of the solid where there is not a gradient of velocity to zero at the surface. In consequence of this, a force is exerted on the solid being the integral round the surface of the force per unit area $\eta (\partial U / \partial r)_{r=a}$, the gradient $\partial U / \partial r$ being measured along a normal to the surface at each point, so that U stands for the component perpendicular to this normal (cf. p. 29).

This force is called "skin-friction" and is a special case of the general hydrodynamic resistance, or drag, F.

Stokes showed that in this case

$$F = 6 \pi a \eta U \quad \cdots \cdots \cdots \quad (21)$$

a being the radius of the sphere and U the undisturbed velocity upstream.

Oseen† makes an approximation to the flow past a sphere when the inertia is not entirely negligible by writing $U + U$ for the component velocity parallel to the main stream and ignoring terms of the second order in U, V, W. The equations then take the form:

$$\left. \begin{aligned} U \frac{\partial U}{\partial x} &= -\frac{1}{\rho} \frac{\partial p}{\partial x} + \nu \nabla^2 U \\ U \frac{\partial V}{\partial x} &= -\frac{1}{\rho} \frac{\partial p}{\partial y} + \nu \nabla^2 V \\ U \frac{\partial W}{\partial x} &= -\frac{1}{\rho} \frac{\partial p}{\partial z} + \nu \nabla^2 W \end{aligned} \right\} \quad \cdots \cdots \quad (22)$$

together with the usual continuity equation (7). This makes at the surface of the sphere $U = -U$, $V = W = 0$. It agrees with (20) except in the distant wake where the flow pattern differs considerably from that near the front stagnation point.

Hele-Shaw's Realisation of Potential Flow with a Viscous Fluid

If a liquid flows between horizontal parallel plates a very small distance apart, the effect of viscous traction is manifest in a vertical plane and prevents the usual action of inertia in a free flow, i.e. the formation of

* *Camb. Trans.*, **8** (1843).   † *Arkiv. f. Math.*, **6**, 29 (1910).

vortices (cf. Chap. 11), while leaving the motion in the x, y plane practically undistorted potential flow. Equations (5) in fact reduce to

$$\eta \frac{\partial^2 U}{\partial z^2} = \frac{\partial p}{\partial x}; \quad \eta \frac{\partial^2 V}{\partial z^2} = \frac{\partial p}{\partial y}; \quad \frac{\partial p}{\partial z} = 0$$

provided we assume $W=0$ and neglect the variation of U and V with x and y in comparison of their variations with z. Also the condition of no slip on the plates requires that

$$\frac{U}{U_0} = \frac{V}{V_0} = \frac{z(2b-z)}{b^2}$$

where U_0 and V_0 are the velocities in the centre of the stratum, $2b$ thick.

Then
$$\frac{\partial^2 U}{\partial z^2} = \frac{-2U_0}{b^2}; \quad \frac{\partial^2 V}{\partial z^2} = \frac{-2V_0}{b^2}$$

and so
$$\frac{\partial p}{\partial x} = kV_0; \quad \frac{\partial p}{\partial y} = kV_0.$$

So that U_0 and V_0 are components of a potential flow.

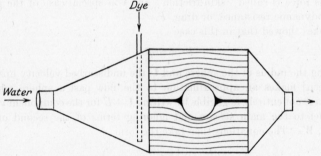

Fig. 5.   Hele-Shaw apparatus for study of potential fields.

Hele-Shaw* set models of obstacles as thin discs in the space between two glass plates $2b$ apart, and by dyed filaments let in to a parallel stream of water between the plates exhibited the potential flow round a number of cylindrical sections in two dimensions, such as the cylinder shown in a plan view of the apparatus in Fig. 5.

The Measurement of Velocity and Pressure in a Stream

(A) Vane anemometers.   When the space occupied by the apparatus is not an objection, anemometers of the rotating vane type may be employed. This is virtually a small windmill with a counter which can be graduated to read the total quantity of air which passes through.

(B) Pitot tube.   If a solid body such as that shown in Fig. 3 be pierced near the front stagnation point and an internal tube be led to a manometer on which one can read the pressure at this point p_1 and compare it with

* *Trans. Inst. Naval Arch.*, **40**, 145 (1898).

that in the absence of flow p_0, the velocity U well upstream can be measured from this pressure excess, for by Bernoulli's principle,

$$p_0 + \tfrac{1}{2}\rho U^2 = p_1$$

A cylinder or sphere such as we have pictured for our "pitot head" would usually be considered to occupy too much space—in a wind tunnel, for example—and the form which a pitot-static combination takes is usually that shown in Fig. 6a, with the dynamic head pointing upstream and the holes for the static measurement facing broadside-on. The pressure differences to be measured may amount to a few millimetres of water, so that a sensitive tilting gauge must be used to measure it with accuracy.

When it is desired to measure the flow close to a solid boundary, "disappearing pitot tubes" of the type used by Stanton *et al.** can be

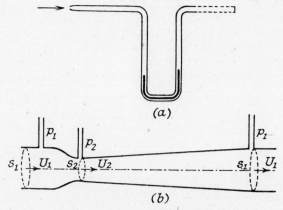

Fig. 6.   (*a*) Pitot, (*b*) Venturi tubes.

made in which one side of the tube projects as a cowling from the solid into the fluid.

(C) **Venturi tube.** The same theorem may be applied to another apparatus for measuring velocity, i.e. that in which the flow is forced through a constriction and in so doing is accelerated. Thus, in Fig. 6b, where the stream of area S_1 and velocity U_1 passes through a throat of area S_2 at speed U_2, the pressure at the latter place must be less by

$$p_1 - p_2 = \tfrac{1}{2}\rho(U_2{}^2 - U_1{}^2) = \tfrac{1}{2}\frac{m^2}{\rho}\left(\frac{1}{S_2{}^2} - \frac{1}{S_1{}^2}\right)$$

In the use m—the mass-flow per second—is often the quantity estimated from a pressure gauge at the constriction.

(D) **Hot-wire anemometer.** This device, the most often used of all for point-to-point measurements of wind or liquid velocity, depends on the

* *Proc. Roy. Soc.*, **A97**, 422 (1920).

cooling experienced by a thin platinum or nickel wire resulting in a change in its electrical resistance. It can also be used to measure fluctuating flow and turbulence. The theory of the use of this instrument is described later under the heading of convection (p. 79).

(E) **Local pressure gauge.** None of these instruments reads the pressure at a point in the flow, though, of course, if the local trend of pressure with velocity is known the former can be derived. For the direct measurement of pressure in a local region on the surface of a solid (the case one is generally most interested in), it is possible to drill holes connected to manometers or to insert a small electrical condenser, one plate of which is fixed in the interior of the obstacle while the other floats with the outer surface and is held flush with it by a spring. Changes in the electrical capacitance of the apparatus with pressure are recorded on a cathode-ray oscillograph, connected in a suitable circuit.

CHAPTER 2

FLUIDS OF SMALL VISCOSITY

We have already mentioned the approximation of Oseen which brings us out of the impasse of d'Alembert, viz. that a body should have no resistance. Another approximation is due to Prandtl, who observed that, with the exception of two regions, the potential pattern of flow round a cylinder is close to reality even when the speed is considerable.

Prandtl* remarked that the viscosity of air is a small quantity, and its effect noteworthy only where the change of velocity from layer to layer is very great. He therefore proposed to neglect viscosity except in a thin layer at the fluid-solid surface. Within this "boundary layer" the tangential velocity rises in a very small distance from 0 at the boundary to the mean velocity of the body of the fluid. Within this layer, stream-line motion should take place even when the motion outside is unsteady.

For example, we may imagine the motion outside the boundary layer to be simple harmonic with respect to time, and due to aerial waves; or to vary from time to time in an incoherent way about an average value in the fashion denoted "turbulent." In order to calculate the thickness of this layer, Prandtl takes a new co-ordinate ζ, normal to the surface in place of y, such that $\zeta=0$ at the surface and $\zeta=\infty$ at the outer edge of the boundary layer. He writes down the equations of motion introducing the viscous term $\eta_1 . dU/d\zeta$ representing the shearing force between adjacent strata of the layer where η_1 is a greatly increased viscosity coefficient consequent on the greatly reduced scale of ζ. In the steady state wherein $dU/dt=0$, it appears that the thickness of the boundary layer depends on $\sqrt{(\eta l/\rho U)}$, where U is the average velocity in the main fluid, ρ is the density, and l is the length, in the direction of the motion, of the surface on which the fluid has rubbed. On inserting the dimensions it will be seen that the above expression is of the dimension of a length, and that the thickness of the boundary layer increases progressively with the square root of the length of the boundary. It is therefore cumulative.

The tangential force of the fluid in the boundary layer integrated round the surface amounts to the "skin-friction" upon it. Measurements of skin-friction will be described later.

Formation of the Wake

We shall continue to cite the circular cylinder as the simplest shape in this connection, though the conclusions will be in general applicable to all obstacles. The ideal motion depicted in Fig. 3 differs from reality

* *Proc. Math. Congress (Heidelberg)* (1904).

in a further respect. Save at indefinitely slow velocities the liquid would not hug the stern of the cylinder in the manner shown by the stream lines, but would cut off part of the corner in the manner shown below (Fig. 7); leaving the cylinder at A, A', and resuming parallel motion at B. The fluid of the shaded area ABA' is "dead water," since it is not carried along by the stream, and the surfaces represented in section by the lines, AB, $A'B$ are "surfaces of discontinuity" to which Helmholtz* ascribed the drag resistance of the cylinder. Owing to the shearing effect of the stream on this dead wake, the fluid in it is set in rotation in the form of two eddies (Figs. 7 and 8, Plate I). That the fluid leaves the solid at A, A' may be ascribed to the intense rates of shear in the boundary layer.

The configuration of the two vortices with the two branches of the stream reuniting persists only for comparatively low velocities. As the speed increases, the vortices extend their bodies and eventually break away to pass downstream. Other vortices form and follow them, so that there is a regular procession of vortices down the stream, forming a "vortex street," and the wake extends indefinitely. These were first noticed by Mallock,† and photographed by Bénard,‡ as dimples on the

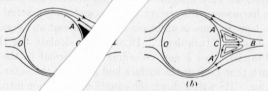

(b)

Fig. 7. Development of wake.

surface of water on which a twig dipped; they may also be seen in air if the obstacle is smeared with a smoke-producing chemical (Fig. 10).

It will be necessary to discuss the stability of such a vortex street. The ideal vortex consists of a core of fluid rotating with constant angular velocity, surrounded by fluid in which there is no rotational velocity. In practice there is no discontinuity in linear velocity at the edge of the vortex, but the motion tails off rather sharply and continuously to the average velocity of the stream. The "strength" of the vortex is defined as twice the product of the angular velocity ω and the cross-section. Consider, first, a single isolated vortex of radius r_0 and of strength K. Then

$$2\pi r_0^2 \omega = K, \text{ from } r=0 \text{ to } r=r_0$$

and

$$\omega = 0, \text{ from } r=r_0 \text{ to } r=\infty$$

Now the linear velocity at a point in the vortex, say, at $r=a$, will be given by $a\omega = Ka/2\pi r_0^2$; thus at the circumference the linear velocity is $K.1/r_0$ normal to the radius. In order that the linear velocity may be

* Ber. Berlin. Akad. Sci. (1868).   † Proc. Roy. Soc. **A 79**, 262 (1907).
‡ Comptes Rendus, **147**, 970 (1908).

continuous at the circumference we must have also at a point outside distant b from the centre, the velocity normal to the radius due to the vortex equal to $r_0^2\omega/b=K/2\pi\,.\,1/b$. Now when a number of vortices exist in a fluid, it is permissible, in order to find the resultant motion at a point due to the system, to superpose vectorially the velocities due to the separate vortices. In particular, if the point in question is the centre of one of the vortices, we can obtain the motion of this one vortex due to all the others. Thus if there are two equal single vortices, one clockwise and one anti-clockwise, distant b apart, each imparts to the other a velocity $K/2\pi b$ in the direction at right angles to the line joining them, and they both move with this velocity, preserving the same relative orientation.

Vortices in Parallel Rows

From the hydrodynamical point of view the case of prime interest is that in which we have an "avenue" of vortices at equal distances apart. Let the vortices in each row be distant l apart, the distance between

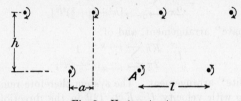

Fig. 9. Vortex street.

the two rows be h, and the amount of "stagger" of one row upon the other be a (Fig. 9).

The velocity imparted to the vortex A in a direction across the avenue by any other vortex in the upper row is

$$\frac{K}{2\pi}\frac{\cos\theta}{\sqrt{[(a+jl)^2+h^2]}}=\frac{K(a+jl)}{2\pi[(a+jl)^2+h^2]}$$

j being any integer and θ the angle between the line joining the vortices and "l." Now the induced velocities due to those in the same row mutually cancel, but those due to the upper row, resolved in the same direction, add up to:

$$U=\frac{K}{2\pi}\left\{\frac{a}{[a^2+h^2]}+\frac{(a+l)}{[(a+l)^2+h^2]}-\frac{(l-a)}{[(l-a)^2+h^2]}+\right.$$
$$\left.\frac{(a+2l)}{[(a+2l)^2+h^2]}-\frac{(2l-a)}{[(l-2a)^2+h^2]}\right\}+\dots\text{ to }\infty$$

This will be equal to zero only in two cases:

(1) $a=0$. The first term of the series is zero, and the alternate positive and negative terms become equal in pairs, and so cancel.

(2) $a=l/2$. Then the first term cancels with the third, the second with the fourth, etc.

If these two cases be imagined pictorially, the first corresponds to vortices opposite to each other in each stream. As far as the corresponding motion produced on any vortex by the rest is concerned, the effects of all those on either side cancel in pairs, leaving only that due to the opposite vortex, and the component of this across the stream is nil, since the velocity produced by this one is entirely in the downstream direction. In the second case, any single vortex is equidistant from the two jth vortices in the other row, counting from the vortex in question. In order, then, that the two series of vortices may remain in parallel rows, every vortex in one row must be oriented symmetrically with respect to the series in the opposite row. Note that although there is then no motion of the vortices across the rows, each and every is actuated with the same velocity along the rows, given by:

$$U = \frac{K}{2\pi} \sum_{j=-\infty}^{j=+\infty} \frac{\sin \theta}{\sqrt{[h^2+(j+\frac{1}{2})^2 l^2]}}$$
$$= \frac{Kh}{2\pi} \sum_{j=-\infty}^{j=+\infty} \frac{1}{[h^2+(j+\frac{1}{2})^2 l^2]}$$

in the "alternate" arrangement, and of:

$$U = \frac{Kh}{2\pi} \sum_{j=-\infty}^{j=+\infty} \frac{1}{(h^2+j^2 l^2)}$$

in the "opposite" arrangement. The system therefore remains in equilibrium, moving with velocity $U=K/2\sqrt{(2)}l$ in the direction of the rows, and with no cross-component (cf. Fig. 10, Plate I).*

Experiment shows that the main production of vortices occurs behind the body, each vortex being formed and then detached to move down the stream after the others in procession at a velocity 0·23 of that of the relative velocity of main stream and cylinder. As long as all have the same initial strength (as we should expect if the velocity of the stream and the position of the cylinder are unchanged), this procession of vortex pairs can remain in equilibrium and move down the stream only if the vortices occupy one or other of the two orientations discussed above; therefore they must be detached periodically from the rear of the cylinder, either in pairs (case 1) or alternately (case 2) from each side. Now although these two possible systems are both equilibrium positions, they are not both stable arrangements.

The calculation of the relative stability of these two equilibrium systems proceeds on the usual lines. One supposes a small displacement ξ_0 given to one of the vortices in the row due to some accidental disturbance, and calculates the net effect on the velocity $d\xi/dt$ of this vortex due to all the others; the solution of the equation for $d\xi/dt$ may be written $\xi=\xi_0 e^{\alpha t}$. The calculation is too abstruse to be given here, but the result shows for

---

* First shown by Kármán and Rubach, *Phys. Zeits.*, **13**, 49 (1912); hence the term "Kármán vortex street."

PLATE I.

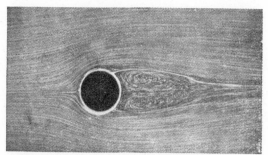

Fig. 8.   Photograph of flow behind circular cylinder.

Fig. 10.   Alternate vortices in wake.

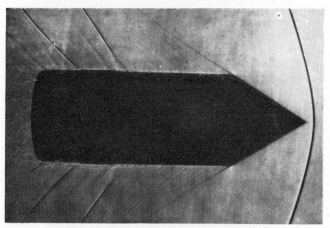

Fig. 45.   Shock waves from projectile.

Fig. 51.   Form of supersonic jet leaving reservoir.

the opposed position, α always positive, any accidental displacement growing with time, system unstable; for the alternate position, α negative, accidental displacements damped out, system stable. Furthermore, in the second case, maximum stability occurs when α has its greatest (negative) value; this occurs when $h/l=0.28$; $h/d=1.21$; $K/Ud=1.7$.

The procession of alternate vortices behind the obstacle imposes a periodic cross-force tending to make it vibrate across the stream. The first scientific investigation of the phenomenon was made by Strouhal.[*] He stretched a wire between the ends of two rods, and an axle parallel to the wire passed through the mid-points of these rods, so that the rotation of the axle whirled the wire through the air round the circumference of a circle, and in a direction at right angles to its length, i.e. the wire described the curved surface of a cylinder. Not only the fundamental of the wire, but harmonics also would respond at appropriate speeds. The connection between the diameter d of the wire, frequency of the tone n, and velocity of the wire through the air U was:

$$\frac{U}{nd}=\text{a constant}$$

This parameter is now known as the Strouhal number. In modern times these motions are investigated by stretching a wire across the wind stream aspirated along a glass-sided wind-tunnel. The vibration of the wire is observed through a telescope, its frequency being established by illuminating it stroboscopically at such a rate that it appears to be stationary. The speed of the draught is calculated from the readings of a pitot-static combination in the tunnel (Richardson[†]).

The modern results establish the constancy of U/nd at a value of 5 for a cylindrical body, except for small values of U or of d. This is noticeable when thin wires (of less than 0·02 cm.) are used; then the "constant" soars up to 8 or more. The lateral extent of the wake depends on the shape of the body, and therefore h alters with the shape, and this affects the value of this constant for bodies of different shape.

Effect of Viscosity on Fluid Vibrations

Experiments made in connection with oscillating wires, or with pendulums in liquids of (kinematic) viscosities varying from 0·01 to 0·5 c.g.s. units, show little or no effect of viscosity on the quantity U/nd, the tones of a wire being produced at practically the same stream velocity in every case. Apparently, then, viscosity does not appreciably change the rate of formation of the Bénard–Kármán vortices. Viscosity has, however, a very important influence on the initiation of the vortex system. There is a minimum velocity below which no vortices, and therefore no tones, are produced. When this critical velocity is exceeded, the stream-lines

[*] *Ann. d. Physik*, **5**, 216 (1878).　　　　[†] *Proc. Phys. Soc.*, **36**, 153 (1924).

can no longer hug the stern, stagnation points appear on the sides, and vorticity in the wake.

This critical velocity then depends on the viscosity and density of the fluid and the width and form of the body, especially of the stern. The two former effects we unite under the coefficient of kinematic viscosity $\nu = \mu/\rho$, the latter pair under a single linear dimension l.

Principle of Dynamical Similarity

The exact form of the dependence of such phenomena on viscosity may be deduced from the method of dimensions. To give a simple illustration of the application of the method: first we will suppose that, as experiment shows, the frequency of the tone depends only on the velocity of the stream and the diameter of the body, so we write $n = f(U, d)$. Now n represents vibrations per unit time, and is of the reciprocal dimensions of time (T^{-1}). U represents distance travelled in unit time, and its dimensions are (L/T). d represents a length (L).

It is necessary that the right-hand side of the equation should have the same dimensions as n, otherwise the equation would depend on the system of units used, e.g. if it were true for metric units it would cease to be valid on changing to English units, therefore $f(U, d)$ must be of dimension $(1/T)$. If we assume that this function can be written out in powers of U and d, say $U^x d^y$, its dimensions are $L^x/T^x.L^y$. In order that this may equal $1/T$ we must have $x = 1$, $y = -1$. Therefore the relation connecting U, n, and d is $n = CU/d$, or $U/nd = $ const., C being a non-dimensional factor.

It is to be noted that this formula does not necessarily apply when some quantity other than U, n, or d is changed—the viscosity of the fluid, for example, or the shape of the tail of the body, a thing we have not taken into account—these things are latent with others in our non-dimensional factor C.

Now let us introduce the viscosity in its common form η, density ρ, and write $n = U^a l^b \eta^c \rho^d$ (the dimensions of η are M/LT, of ρ are M/L^3); proceeding as before, and equating powers

$$\text{of } M; \quad c = -d$$
$$\text{of } L; \quad 0 = a+b+2c$$
$$\text{of } T; \quad -1 = -a-c$$

whence
$$a = 1-c, \quad b = -c-1$$

so that $n = U^{1-c} d^{-c-1} \eta^c \rho^{-c} = U/d (\nu/Ud)^c$, putting $\nu = \eta/\rho$. There are not enough equations to determine c and this may be given any value, or we may write this in the general form:

$$\frac{U}{nd} = C'f\left(\frac{Ud}{\nu}\right)$$

where C' now is a non-dimensional constant not involving viscosity.

The form of the function $f(Ud/\nu)$ could be found from results in fluids of different viscosity.   Our results indicate that it is $(Ud/\nu)^0$, or independent of viscosity over practically the whole range investigated, but that the periodic shedding of vortices to which n is due starts at a definite value of Ud/ν.

The evidence for the last statement is as follows.   With a string tuned to a definite pitch n, it is generally possible to get a vibration when U/nd is 5.   As the tension in the string is released, n and U for this tone fall, until at a definite value of n no tone is produced at the appropriate value of U.   The inference is that the motion has become steady—vortices have ceased to be produced.   The values of Ud/ν when the tones failed to be heard were collected by the author and found to cluster round the value 30 for a cylinder and 60 for a rubber cord of streamlined section.

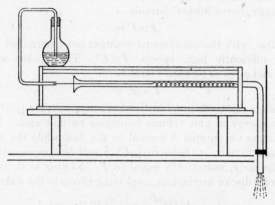

Fig. 11.   Osborne Reynolds apparatus.

Here, for a moment, we must leave the discussion of wakes to go back to an earlier observation.   In a classical research, Osborne Reynolds allowed water to flow along a horizontal glass pipe into which he introduced axially at the entrance a filament of ink from a siphon (cf. his original drawing, Fig. 11).   When the mean velocity in the pipe was sufficiently low he found that the ink remained as a thread throughout the tube, indicating stream-line flow, but when a critical velocity was reached the ink began to churn up at some point in the tube and to mix with the water, indicating eddying flow.   This change occurred always at the same value of the parameter Ud/ν—about 2,000, where U was the mean velocity of the water and d the diameter of the pipe.   (He varied ν by altering the temperature of the water.)   This parameter, which we have already met in discussing the alternate vortices in a wake, is now known as Reynolds number.

* *Phil. Trans.*, **174**, 935 (1883).

Hydrodynamic Resistance or Drag

The formation of a wake with rotating masses of fluid involves a transfer of energy, eventually into heat, and this dissipation occurs at the expense of the work done in moving the obstacle through the fluid, i.e. against the resisting force (F) or drag of the body. This eddy-making resistance is over and above the skin-friction companion to drag in the boundary layer already instanced. Treating this case dimensionally, let us put

$$F \propto d^v U^w \rho^y \eta^z$$

In dimensional terms, this becomes:

$$[MLT^{-2}] = L^v [LT^{-1}]^w [ML^{-3}]^y [ML^{-1}T^{-1}]^z$$

but is not adequate to determine all the four exponents. So we appeal to the results of experiment and say:

(A) At sufficiently low speeds, $F \propto U$—this makes $v=1$, $w=1$, $z=1$—and eventually derive Stokes' formula

$$F \propto U d \eta$$

but, of course, with the unexpressed constant not determined.

(B) At sufficiently high speeds, $F \propto U^2$. This makes $w=2$, $x=2$, $y=1$, $z=0$ and gives us Newton's formula:

$$F \propto \rho U^2 d^2$$

This formula can be deduced in Newton's own way, for $\frac{1}{2}\rho U^2$ represents the kinetic energy of unit volume impinging on unit area. The energy which impinges on an area S normal to the flow while the fluid moves forward unit distance is therefore $\frac{1}{2}\rho U^2 . S$ and this represents the work done on the body, numerically equal to F. Newton so derived for the resistance of a disc or hemisphere, neglecting effects in the wake, the value

$$\frac{1}{2}\rho U^2 \frac{\pi d^2}{4} \quad \text{or} \quad \frac{\pi}{8}\rho U^2 d^2$$

A back pressure in the wake reduces the experimental value below this. It is customary, anyhow, to express drag in the form

$$F = c_D (\tfrac{1}{2}\rho U^2) S$$

where S is the surface presented by the body and is generally reckoned as its projected area perpendicular to the flow, e.g. $\pi d^2/4$ for a sphere. c_D is the drag coefficient and is a constant for the shape at a particular Reynolds number.

The drag on a cylinder per unit length in the stage of the periodic vortex detachment can be approximately deduced starting from the premise that the component of the impulse in any direction necessary to generate from rest the field of a straight vortex of strength K is $\rho K h$ per unit length, where h is the width of the field. If vortices are set up at a frequency n per second, the total impulse per second is

$$n\rho K h = 2\frac{nd}{U} \cdot \frac{K}{Ud} \cdot \frac{h}{d} \cdot \frac{\rho U^2 d}{2} = 2 \times 0 \cdot 2 \times 1 \cdot 7 \times 1 \cdot 21 (\tfrac{1}{2}\rho U^2 d)$$

using the numerical values for these parameters given on previous pages. This gives a value of 0·82 for the drag coefficient of the cylinder against a mean experimental value of 0·90.

The drag coefficient for a cylinder at various values of Reynolds number Re (plotted logarithmically) is shown on Fig. 12 (continuous line). The large values attributed to low Reynolds numbers derive from the fact that in this region the drag is really proportional to U and not to U^2, as we have assumed in our manner of exhibiting the coefficient. At very low $Re<1$, White[*] has shown that the drag of a cylinder no longer depends on the density of the fluid, but very much on the nature and position of the outer boundaries of the fluid medium. On the same graph we have exhibited (broken line) the variations of the reciprocal of Strouhal number to exemplify, in accordance with the conclusions of the preceding

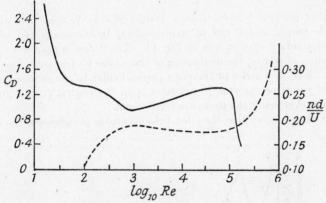

Fig. 12. Drag coefficient and Strouhal number for circular cylinder.

paragraph, its intimate connection with the drag, at least over the range $40<Re<3\times10^6$.

The changes in c_D at high Re are connected with changes in the wake and the flow round the body, which we must now discuss in some detail.

Form of the Wake and its Relation to Conditions in the Boundary Layer

The tracks of the vortices in the wake as they move downstream can be followed by using a hot wire as detector. As they pass over the wire alternate heating and cooling ensues, which after amplification may be made to excite a vibration galvanometer tuned to the Strouhal frequency n, or to produce the same tone in a loudspeaker. The maximum response of the detecting apparatus occurs when it is so placed as to be struck by

[*] *Proc. Roy. Soc.*, **A186**, 472 (1945).

the cores of the vortices. Fig. 13 (after Tyler*) shows the vortex street behind a circular cylinder traced by hot-wire detectors in this way, the vortices at first approaching and then opening out slightly as they recede.

The longitudinal spacing of the eddies can be discovered by using two hot wires in tandem, each connected to one of the primaries of a split-transformer and noting the current induced in the secondary coil. Fig. 14 (also from Tyler*) shows the result on the induced current of keeping one wire fixed just behind the cylinder "on one side of the street" and moving

Fig. 13. Longitudinal traverse of a vortex "street."

the other gradually downstream. During this movement the primary currents march in and out of step, resulting in the peaks and troughs in the secondary current seen in Fig. 14. The decay in successive peaks represents, of course, the dissipation of the eddies by friction. The same effect is seen in a series of traverses perpendicular to the stream, for the sides of the street become less distinct from the central portion further back and eventually the peaks are levelled out.

Piercy† has shown that the pitot tube is capable of indicating the width

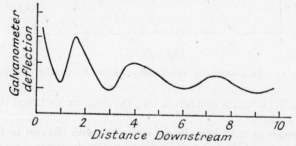

Fig. 14. Lateral traverse of vortex "street."

of a vortex street if the static pressure variations are ignored and the *total* dynamic head measured from point to point across the wake. Wherever, on traversing the pitot tube across a stream, it remains sensibly constant, it can be inferred that there is no vorticity in this region.

Conditions in the wake are really due to changes in the régime of flow alongside the cylinder, i.e. in the boundary layer. This layer was originally pictured by Prandtl as a laminar skin round the solid even when

* *Phil. Mag.*, **11**, 848 (1931).   † *J. Roy. Aero. Soc.* (1923).

the stream further out was turbulent. If U is the mean velocity outside the skin of thickness ζ, we can speak of $U\zeta/\nu$ as the local Reynolds number of the boundary layer. But eventually a local Re may be reached at which the shearing forces in the boundary layer are so great that it, too, becomes turbulent. This transition is, however, influenced by other

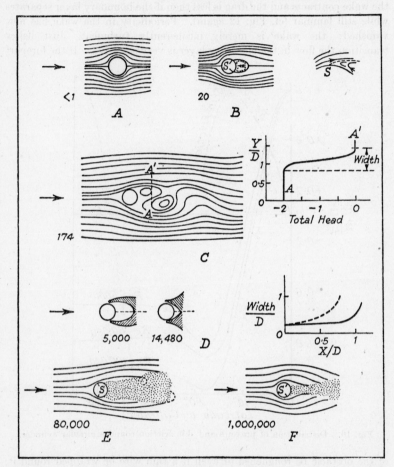

Fig. 15. Development of flow and related drag coefficient (*reproduced by permission of the University of Pennsylvania*).

factors, such as the intensity of turbulence in the free stream (*vide infra*), the pressure gradient round the surface and its roughness. For a bluff body, the transition is associated with but is not usually identical with the breakaway point at which the main stream leaves the cylinder, accompanied by a reversal of direction of flow near the surface to pass downstream enclosing a wake.   Between $Re=5,000$ and $Re=15,000$ (values for the whole cylinder) the layer increases in thickness generally, c_D rises until the point of transition reaches the point of secession, when it remains constant for a while (Fig. 12).   At values of Re near 10^5 transition to turbulence is definite; it delays separation to points further astern, the wake contracts and the drag is less than if the boundary layer separates while still laminar (cf. Fig. 12 again).   Periodicity in the wake has now vanished: the wake is merely incoherently turbulent.   Just below transition the flow in the boundary layer is very sensitive.   If the forepart

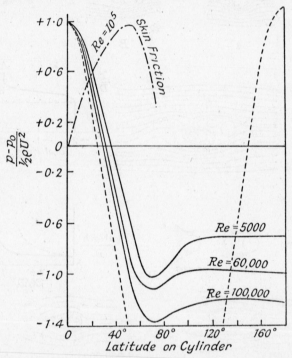

Fig. 16.   Distribution of pressure and skin friction round a circular cylinder.

of the obstacle be roughened or even if a thin wire be wrapped round it, transition occurs and the resistance can be lowered.   Fig. 15 (after Dryden*) shows the main changes in the flow which occur as Re is increased. The extent of the turbulent region can in each case be traced by the pitot defect as already mentioned.   The Reynolds number corresponding to each régime is given beneath each sketch.   To the right of B is shown the form of the breakaway occurring at the zone S, where we see the reversed

* *Univ. of Pennsylvania Bicent. Conf.* (1941).

flow from the wake vortices meeting the main flow where it separates. To the right of C is given a traverse of total head deficit across the section AA', with the co-ordinate Y expressed as a fraction of D, the diameter of the obstacle; the head rises steeply through the region affected by the vortex near A' to its value in the open stream. At D, we have the change in the configuration of the turbulent wake at $Re=10^5$, which causes the reduction in c_D aforesaid. The width of the eddying wake grows at different rates downstream as the offset shows in terms of X/D, X being distance downstream. At E there is transition to turbulence in the boundary layer at the point of separation of the fluid and at F transition in the boundary layer *before* separation.

The steepness of the velocity gradient in the boundary layer is paralleled by the value of the normal pressure. In the case of the circular cylinder, this pressure can be measured by a hole drilled in the surface, connected to a manometer, with the hole rotated to various azimuths in turn. Fig. 16 shows results obtained in this way for a circular cylinder at various Reynolds numbers compared with the classical values in potential flow. The latter is shown by dotted line and actually falls to -3 at $90°$. The "pressure defect"—expressed as a ratio to $\frac{1}{2}\rho U^2$—falls from 1 at latitude $0°$ (front stagnation point) to zero at about $45°$ and reaches a negative maximum at $70°$, thereafter subsiding to a nearly constant negative value, dependent on the value of Re, i.e. on the amount of vorticity in the wake.

When the boundary layer remains laminar the skin-friction may be calculated from such readings of the normal pressure. This is shown as a chain line on Fig. 16 for the forward portion of the cylinder. In this region it agrees fairly well with the approximate calculations of Thom,[*] of Green,[†] and of Falkner and Skan.[‡] The former author has also shown that up to $Re=10^4$ the skin-frictional drag coefficient is well represented by the expression $4/\sqrt{Re}$. Measurements of the velocity round a circular cylinder have been made by the author[§] using hot-wire anemometers (*vide infra*, p. 79). From plots of velocity along normals to the cylinder, contour lines of equal velocity—expressed in ratio to the undisturbed stream—may be constructed. Fig. 17 shows a typical set at $Re=500$, on which the separation and wake can be clearly seen.

Transition to turbulence occurs nearer to the cylinder as the speed increases. A more intimate study of this phenomenon is gained by observing the fluctuations in the current through a hot wire, exhibited on a string galvanometer or cathode-ray oscillograph (cf. p. 80). Fig. 18 gives contours of equal velocity amplitude in the boundary layer of a cylinder at $Re=2\times10^4$ (Piercy and Richardson‖).

* A.R.C., R. and M., 1176 (1928). † Ibid., 1313 (1930).
‡ Ibid., 1314 (1930). § Ibid., 1368 (1931).
‖ Phil. Mag., **5**, 6 (1928).

The Boundary Layer of a Flat Plate

The velocity U outside the boundary layer being supposed constant (undisturbed flow) we neglect in the latter $\partial^2 U/\partial x^2$ in comparison with $\partial^2 U/\partial y^2$ and obtain the equations:

$$U\frac{\partial U}{\partial x}+V\frac{\partial U}{\partial y}=\nu\frac{\partial^2 U}{\partial y^2} \qquad (23)$$

with $U=\partial\psi/\partial y$ and $V=-\partial\psi/\partial x$, and the boundary conditions $U=U$, at $y=\infty$, $x=0$.

Prandtl saw that a solution of these equations could be obtained in which the stream function depended on ζ only, if $\zeta=\frac{1}{2}(U/\nu x)^{\frac{1}{2}}y$. That is to say, if the co-ordinate perpendicular to the plate be multiplied by the parameter $\sqrt{(U/\nu x)}$, all motions along flat plates become similar;

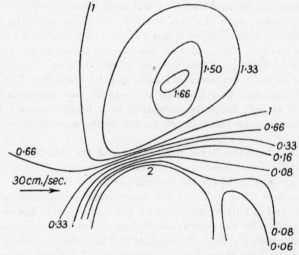

Fig. 17. Plot of velocity field round a circular cylinder in stream.

$U/\nu x$ is, in fact, the Reynolds number of the flow at this point. Blasius[*] later gave a justification of this, pointing out that if a flat plate in stationary fluid is suddenly moved with a constant velocity U, in its own plane, the velocity of the fluid at any distance y from this plane after time t is

$$U=U\left[1-\frac{2}{\sqrt{\pi}}\int_0^{y/2\sqrt{(\nu t)}}e^{-y^2/4\nu t}d\left(\frac{y}{2\sqrt{(\nu t)}}\right)\right] \quad \text{(cf. p. 48)}$$

so that the stress on unit area of the plate:

$$-\eta\left[\frac{\partial U}{\partial y}\right]_{y=0}=\rho U\sqrt{\frac{\nu}{\pi t}}$$

The upper limit in the integral agrees with Prandtl's parameter if we replace t by its equivalent—in terms of the plate's movement—x/U.

[*] *Z. f. Math. u. Phys.*, **56**, 4 (1908).

The flow along a flat plate edge-on to the wind has been explored by Hansen* using pitot tubes and by van der Hegge Zijnen† using hot-wire anemometers. The former measurements are in good agreement with

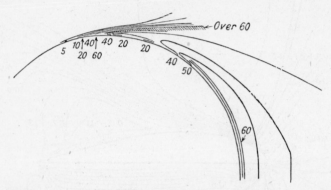

Fig. 18.   Contours of velocity amplitude round a cylinder in a stream.

boundary layer theory, as Fig. 19 shows, except near the leading edge. (In this figure the symbols refer to different values of x from the leading edge.)   Fig. 20 shows the contours of velocity as measured by Piercy and Richardson‡ for the flow round an aerofoil at $Re = 2 \times 10^4$.   The flow over

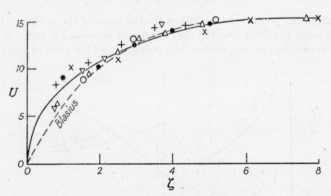

Fig. 19.   Velocities (in non-dimensional form) along flat plate in a stream.

$$\begin{array}{ccccccc} & \times & O & + & \bullet & \triangledown & \triangle \\ x = & 4 & 8 & 12 & 23 & 33 & 43 \text{ cm.} \end{array}$$

the lower flat surface corresponds to that of the flat plate, but breakaway ensues over the upper surface before the fluid reaches the trailing edge.

* Z. f. Ange. Math. u. Mech., 8, 185 (1928).   ‡ A.R.C., R. and M., 1224 (1928).
† Proc. Int. Congress App. Mech., 113 (1924).

(N.B.—To make the contours clear, dimensions perpendicular to the surface have been exaggerated 8 times in comparison with those along it.)

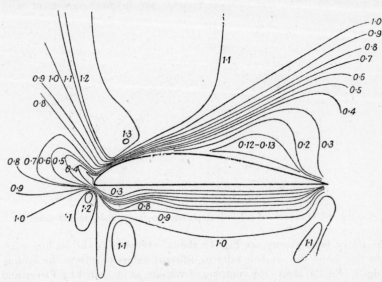

Fig. 20. Contours of velocity round aerofoil section in a stream (*distances normal to surface magnified 8 times*).

Owing to the progressive change in the thickness of the boundary layer passing along the flat plate, the drag coefficient expressed in terms of unit length in two-dimensional motion fails steadily until the point of transition

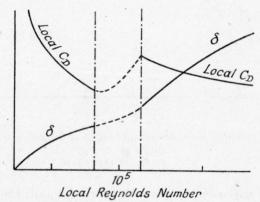

Fig. 21. Distribution of c_D and boundary layer thickness along plate.

is reached when it jumps up to fall again steadily t hrough the turbulent layer. Fig. 21 shows how c_D varies along the u nderside of the aerofoil, together with δ, the thickness of the boundary layer. The point of transition is a little indefinite, fluctuating about a local Re of 10^5 within the region delineated by the two vertical lines. The actual value of Re at which the jump occurs depends on the amount of turbulence initially present in the wind-tunnel and the vagaries of the point of transition must be due to casual variations in the eddy content of the stream near the plate.

Boundary Layers in Pipes

The progressive growth in thickness of the boundary layer of a pipe from the entry may be followed also by the use of pitot tubes or hot

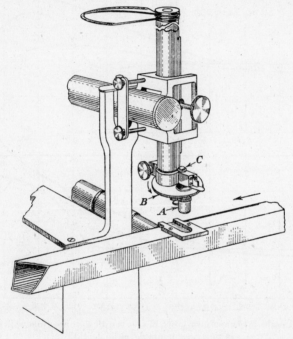

Fig. 22. Ultramicroscope apparatus of Fage.

wires. In another method due to Fage and Townend* the actual motion of suspended particles in the stream of air in a glass-walled pipe is observed by a microscope of which the objective is given a short passage with or across the stream. Those "mites" which lie in the focal plane and have the same velocity as the objective will then appear stationary in the eye-piece. In this way, Fage plotted the velocity distribution in the three co-ordinate planes near the wall of the pipe.

Fage's apparatus is shown in Fig. 22. The microscope objective A turns with the brass disc B at constant speed about the pivot C. Below

* *Proc. Roy. Soc.*, **A135**, 656 (1932).

is the miniature pipe in which the flow is taking place, looked at by the observer through a glass window let into its upper wall immediately beneath the microscope.

Knowing the mean speed U_0 in the pipe of effective depth m or its value at the place of observation U, it is possible to calculate the root-mean-square deviations, u, v, w in the three co-ordinate directions with and across the general drift and to express these in ratio to the mean speed (Fig. 23). It will be noticed that all these fluctuations increase as the wall is approached, due presumably to the sharp shearing in its vicinity.

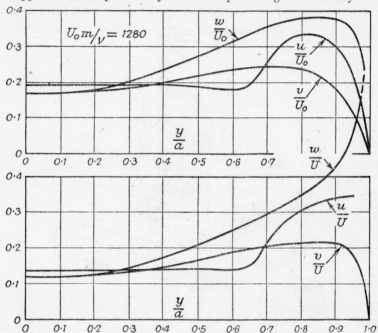

Fig. 23. Results in channel; variation of u, v, w with distance from wall (a=radius of pipe; m=hydraulic mean depth).

The Boundary Layer of Rotating Cylinders

If to the potential flow round a cylinder of radius a in a stream of velocity U we impose a circulation, we derive a cross-force from the asymmetry of the flow (cf. Fig. 3d). The resulting potential $\phi = U(r + a^2/r) \cos \theta + cU\theta$, where c is the ratio of peripheral velocity to U. This circulation may be produced by rotating the cylinder about its axis in virtue of the viscous traction exerted through the boundary layer. The potential theory demands that the circulation shall be constant at all distances so that an isolated cylinder (not in a stream) should induce a tangential velocity U at a radial distance r such that Ur is constant.

In fact, the velocity falls off more rapidly than this, especially in the boundary layer close to the surface of the cylinder, but reaches this condition at several diameters distant from the surface.

In two-dimensional laminar motion about the axis of the cylinder, if we consider unit depth of fluid parallel to the axis, the rate of shear at a radius r, where the angular velocity is ω, is $r \cdot \partial \omega / \partial r$, and therefore the force due to friction is $\eta r \cdot d/dr \, (U/r)$ per unit area (cf. p. 12). Hence the work done in a circumferential displacement l

$$= \eta r l^2 \frac{d}{dr}\left(\frac{U}{r}\right) = \eta l^2 \left(\frac{dU}{dr} + \frac{U}{r}\right) \quad . \quad . \quad . \quad . \quad (24)$$

The quantity in brackets is the difference of velocity between two annuli at unit distance apart.

Rayleigh* pointed out that in rotational motion of this type there will be a difference of centrifugal force at different annuli, which has to be reckoned with in examining the stability of the system. This difference for two annuli at unit distance apart will be

$$\frac{\rho\left[Ur\left(\dfrac{dU}{dr} + \dfrac{U}{r}\right)\right]^2}{r+1} - \frac{\rho U^2}{r} = 2\rho\frac{U}{r}\left(\frac{dU}{dr} + \frac{U}{r}\right)$$

approximately, per unit volume. In a displacement l the mean difference of centrifugal force will be $l/2$ times this (in virtue of the unit breadth and depth of the volume in question), and therefore the work done against centrifugal force will be

$$\rho l^2 \frac{U}{r}\left(\frac{dU}{dr} + \frac{U}{r}\right) \quad . \quad . \quad . \quad . \quad . \quad (25)$$

(24) and (25) together give the energy in the fluid annulus. We may use the principle of minimum energy, enunciated by Kelvin and James Thomson, to find the velocity distribution round the cylinder. Assuming $U = U_0(r/a)^n$, where U_0 is the velocity at the surface of the cylinder of radius a, we then have

$$l^2\left(\frac{dU}{dr} + \frac{U}{r}\right)\left(\eta + \rho\frac{U}{r}\right)$$

a minimum if $(n+1)r^{n-1}(\eta + \rho r^{n-1})$ is a minimum.

This quantity is in fact 0 if $n = -1$. The potential distribution of velocity, $U = U_0 a/r$, therefore satisfies this case.

Centrifugal force may, however, cause mixing of the fluid in neighbouring annuli, especially in the boundary layer of the cylinder, where U^2/r is high. If this happens the equation for the frictional energy will no longer be (24), but will be that derived from the shearing stress in turbulent motion.

Osborne Reynolds† evaluated this stress as $\rho \overline{uv}$ where u and v are the deviations from the steady velocities in rectangular directions induced

---

* *Proc. Roy. Soc.*, **A93**, 148 (1916).   † *Phil. Trans.*, **A186**, 123 (1895).

by the turbulent motion. Further, the disturbance of velocity v along a radius will be proportional to the tangential deviation u producing it.

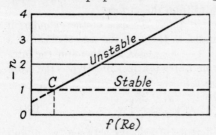

Fig. 24. Stability in velocity gradient near rotating cylinder.

The work done for a displacement l is accordingly proportional to

$$\rho l^2 \left(\frac{dU}{dr} + \frac{U}{r} \right) \left(\frac{dU}{dr} + \frac{U}{r} \right) \quad (26)$$

For the factor of proportionality we may select some quantity which will be a function of Reynolds number $f(Re)$.

Taking now (25) with (26), we have to choose the velocity distribution so that

$$\rho l^2 \left(\frac{dU}{dr} + \frac{U}{r} \right) \left\{ \frac{U}{r} + \frac{1}{f(Re)} \left(\frac{dU}{dr} + \frac{U}{r} \right) \right\} \quad \cdots \quad (27)$$

is a minimum.

Substituting $U = U_0 (r/a)^n$ as before, we obtain

$$- \rho l^2 \cdot \frac{U_0}{a^n} \{ (n+1)[f(Re)+n+1)] \} \quad \cdots \quad (28)$$

This is 0 if $n = -1$ or $-f(Re)-1$.

In this case it seems natural to take $U_0 a / \nu$ for the appropriate Reynolds number and write, to a first approximation,

$$f(Re) = \left[\frac{U_0 a}{\nu} \right]^m$$

The value of Re at which this second solution coincides with the first (C on Fig. 24) will be the critical value for this type of flow. More exactly, there will be a critical velocity for each annulus, and the Re in question will be the appropriate value of Ur/ν for the given annulus of fluid, rotating with a velocity U at a distance r from the axis.*

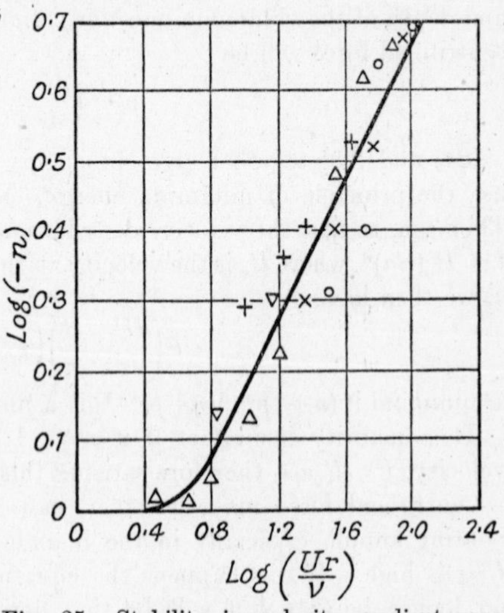

The author† made some measurements of velocity round two isolated rotating cylinders,

Fig. 25. Stability in velocity gradient near rotating cylinder.

$\frac{1}{2}$ and 1 inch diameter respectively. Results showed no fixed value of the exponent n for a given cylinder rotated at a given speed; n is, as

* *Phil. Mag.*, **11**, 1215 (1931).   † *A.R.C., R. and M.*, 1368 (1931).

indicated, a function of the local Reynolds number of the annulus in question, not of the cylinder itself. The experimental values of n are plotted in log form against Re in Fig. 25 for comparison with the theoretical ones of Fig. 24. (The symbols refer to different rotational speeds and cylinders.)

In the same way, when a rotating cylinder is placed in an erstwhile uniform stream, the full theoretical lift given by application of Bernoulli's principle (cf. p. 7) is not attained in practice owing to viscous dissipation. Fig. 26 shows some measured lift and drag coefficients for various values of the ratio c (peripheral velocity U/undisturbed stream velocity U). The theoretical lift is $\rho UK = \rho U(\pi aU) = \frac{1}{2}\rho U^2 \times 2\pi aU$ per unit length, so on this basis the lift coefficient should equal πc.

It is also worthy of note that c_D falls at first as the cylinder is rotated. This may be linked with changes in the wake, where the alternate vortices

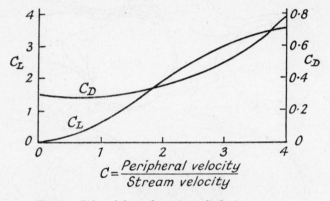

Fig. 26.   Lift and drag of rotating cylinder in a stream.

are no longer equal in strength though their combined vorticity is less than with no rotation (cf. Fig. 27, where the contours are of equal velocity amplitude, with Fig. 18). The difference in positive and negative vorticity is retrieved in the circulation round the cylinder.

Manipulation of the Boundary Layer

From what has been written, it is evident that the drag of a bluff-shaped body depends on the strength and width of its eddying wake, which in turn depends on the point of separation and so on the transition to turbulence in the erstwhile laminar boundary layer. In fact, the drag coefficient of a smooth sphere as determined in different wind-tunnels is used as a measure of the amount of turbulence therein.

It is also evident that a reduction of the drag of a bluff obstacle can be effected if the width of the band of vorticity can be reduced.

Some of the earliest and most successful attempts at control in the boundary layer aimed at the inhibition of breakaway by pushing or pulling the fluid round the bluff portions of the obstacle. They all try to reduce the eddy-making resistance and leave the profile drag almost unchanged

Schrenck* used a sphere 1 foot in diameter, mounted in a wind-channel, and having ring-shaped slots contrived in the rear half, from which air was exhausted by way of a hollow tube of the force balance through a pump to the outside air. Smoke mixed with the air showed the extent of the turbulent wake. The reduction in drag coefficient is shown in the following table.

Reynolds number	2×10^5	3×10^5	4×10^5
Drag coefficient without suction	0·40	0·15	0·12
„ „ with suction .	0·09	0·08	0·12

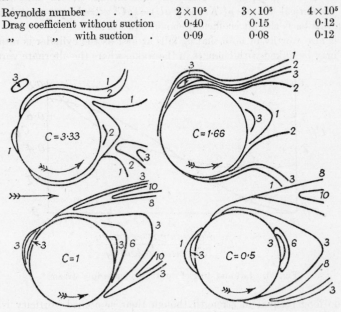

Fig. 27.   Contours of velocity round rotating cylinder in a stream.

Besides a diminution of vorticity in the wake due to the restriction imposed on the expansion of the boundary layer, a suction device also changes the general distribution of pressure round the model, since it acts as a sink whose effects are experienced both fore and aft of the orifice. That is why the location of the slit, though relatively unimportant from the aspect of the prevention of turbulence in the boundary layer itself, does modify the reduction in drag which one would anticipate.

Other investigators have tried to increase the circulation and inhibit a breakaway by pumping air out of holes contrived in the fore part of the model and directed towards the tail. Reid and Bamber† studied a

* *Zeits. f. Motorluftschiffart.*, **17**, 386 (1926); *Luftfahrtforschung*, **12**, 11 (1935).
† *N.A.C.A., Tech. Note* No. 286.

number of such devices experimentally, but came to the conclusion that suction is more economical than compression for drag reduction.

Abbott* constructed what he called an internal circulation wing not requiring the use of a pump in which air was taken into the hollow interior through a slit near the front stagnation point and released through a number of narrow slits on the upper side beyond the section of maximum thickness. The useful range of lift/drag was so increased, but the maximum lift was reduced as compared with an untouched model of the same size and shape. Indeed, it is probably impossible to increase the maximum lift without supplying additional kinetic energy to the air from a pump, or external booster of circulation.

In more recent developments, suction is applied over an area of the wing, through a cluster of slots or holes, where adverse pressure gradients may be expected. It has also been found that when a body is moving through the air at speeds approaching the velocity of sound, suction may be usefully employed to delay the rise in drag which occurs at such speeds (cf. Chap. 3).

Periodic Boundary Layers

As a stage between laminar and turbulent boundary layers of particular importance for explaining how the transition comes about, we must study the effect on a steady stream of imposing on it a simple harmonic motion. There are various ways of doing this: a solid boundary may be given a to-and-fro motion as a whole as the fluid streams steadily past it; or a vibrating element of it may give a local oscillation to the boundary layer; or, finally, the solid walls may be still but of a wavy surface, whereby the fluid in the layer is forced into sinusoidal motion as it passes nearby. On a larger scale the boundary layer of a flag flapping in the wind produces the same kind of disturbance.

When alternating flow is taking place through an orifice, as at the mouth of an acoustic resonator, the velocity amplitude rises from the edge of the orifice to a peak and thereafter falls gradually to a mean towards the centre. This "annular effect" is similar to the skin effect shown by alternating electric currents in a conductor, and is still shown when a direct current (in the electric or hydrodynamic sense) is superposed on the alternating flow (Richardson†).

To demonstrate this we must transform the Navier–Stokes equations into cylindrical co-ordinates. They become, for a circular tube stretching along the axis of x:

$$\frac{\partial U}{dt} = X - \frac{1}{\rho}\frac{\partial p}{\partial r} + \nu\left(\frac{\partial^2 U}{\partial r^2} + \frac{1}{r}\frac{\partial U}{\partial r}\right)$$

* N.A.C.A., Tech. Note No. 371.
† Proc. Phys. Soc., **40**, 206 (1928); cf. Sexl, Zeits. f. Phys., **61**, 349 (1930).

Setting the applied force in S.H.M. form as

$$X-\frac{1}{\rho}\frac{\partial p}{\partial x}=Ce^{i\omega t}$$

we obtain

$$\frac{d^2U}{dr^2}+\frac{1}{r}\frac{dU}{dr}-\frac{i\omega}{\nu}U+\frac{C}{\nu}=0 \quad \cdots \quad (29)$$

the solution of which is

$$U=-\frac{iC}{\omega}\left[1-\frac{J_0\sqrt{(-i\omega/\nu).r}}{J_0\sqrt{(-i\omega/\nu).a}}\right]e^{i\omega t}. \quad \cdots \quad (30)$$

With low-frequency pulsation the arguments of the Bessel functions can be replaced by series up to their second terms, and

$$U=-\frac{iC}{\omega}\left[1-\frac{1+(i\omega/4\nu)r^2}{1+(i\omega/4\nu)a^2}\right]\cos \omega t$$

of which the real part is

$$\frac{C}{4\nu}.(a^2-r^2)\cos \omega t \quad \cdots \quad \cdots \quad (31)$$

If, on the other hand, these arguments are large, the second term in the bracket of (30) can be neglected except for those particles in a boundary layer close to the wall of the tube (where $r \to a$). Then the real part is

$$U=\frac{C}{\omega}\sin \omega t$$

Within the boundary layer we replace $a-r$ with ζ (*vide supra*) and obtain

$$U=\frac{C}{\omega}\sin \omega t-\frac{C}{\omega}e^{-\sqrt{(\omega/2\nu)}\zeta}\sin [\omega t-\sqrt{(\omega/2\nu)}\zeta] \quad \cdots \quad (32)$$

showing that damped waves travel out from the wall with velocity $\sqrt{(2/\omega\nu)}$ and damping coefficient $\sqrt{(\omega/2\nu)}$. Fig. 28 shows a plot of the velocity amplitude across a tube in alternating flow at various frequencies, n, induced by acoustic means. U reaches a maximum amplitude where $\sqrt{(\omega/2\nu)}=2.28/\zeta$. On either side of this critical distance the amplitude falls; to zero at the wall and to the "mainstream" value C/ω at a moderate distance out.

The experimental method which this line of thought suggests is to impose on a steady stream an S.H.M. of small amplitude and moderate frequency and to examine the transformation of the flow by this superposed fluctuation to see how closely it approximates in properties to a naturally turbulent stream, particularly in respect of (1) rise and decay of the fluctuations and (2) development of characteristic distribution of velocity across the stream. The devices which have been employed to produce the desired S.H.M. in the course of the fluid comprise: (1) tangential oscillation of part of a smooth wall over which the fluid passes; (2) passage of the fluid over a rigid corrugated solid boundary; (3) passage over a flexible boundary. The latter may take the form of a pennant, or the fluid may be forced out of a linear orifice to impinge on a wedge so that the jet is set in sinusoidal oscillation between fluid boundaries, as in the familiar method of producing edge tones.

Most illuminating from the point of view of the architecture of turbulence are the experiments of the first type, in which a pipe has a loose section interposed between the entrance cone and the main portion of the pipe, which is connected at its other end to an aspirator. The loose section is mounted on the end of a long connecting-rod to a crank with adjustable throw on the axle of an electric motor. Air is first aspirated through the pipe at a speed just below the critical value and the gradient of velocity explored at various sections of the pipe downstream from the mobile

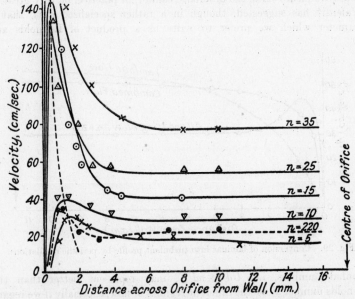

Fig. 28. Velocity amplitude in alternating flow in tube.

portion. This is next set in operation and the velocity traverses redetermined. Whereas the former profile was parabolic, it has now gone over into the steeper logarithmic type characteristic of turbulent flow, which can in fact be reproduced in the untouched flow in the pipe by making the entry more abrupt, or copied at a larger scale by increasing the speed of aspiration above the critical, cf. Fig. 29 (Richardson and Tyler*).

It may be objected that this artificial turbulence does not correspond with nature in that the pulsatance ω is not monochromatic in real turbulence but is more like a band spectrum, embracing a range of frequencies requiring a Fourier series in the solution (*vide infra*). To

* *Phys. Zeits.*, **32**, 509 (1931).

the extent that such partial vibrations may in practice have different damping coefficients so that the spectrum changes *en marchant*, our idealised picture of turbulent flow requires modification; but it is certainly a fact that natural turbulence shows velocity profiles and distribution of intensity of fluctuation precisely similar to those in our developed flow. Thus Fage and Townend* in their ultra-microscopic investigation of turbulent flow in pipes have found peaks in the fluctuations near the walls like those shown here in Fig. 28 (cf. Fig. 23). Also, measurements of the correlation between fluctuations at different points as the stream progresses seem to indicate that their spectrum changes quite slowly, so that although one would expect the high-frequency partials to be more rapidly damped than the low-frequency ones, the difference cannot, in practice, be very great.

Valensi† has suggested, though in a rather specialised case, that a parameter which we prefer to write as a product of Reynolds and

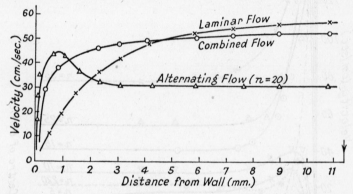

Fig. 29.   Conversion of laminar into turbulent profile by periodic oscillations.

Strouhal numbers, i.e. $Ud/\nu \times nd/U$, may represent better than the Reynolds number alone the different régimes of flow, especially if we regard the development of turbulence as due to the onset of oscillations in an erstwhile steady flow.

As a further test of the applicability of these concepts to turbulence, various aerodynamic models, e.g. a cylinder and a streamlined strut, were placed in a wind-tunnel with the speed insufficient to produce turbulence in the boundary layer of the model, and the whole surface (in the case of the cylinder) or a small vibrating element near the nose (in the case of the strut) given a small oscillation at various frequencies from 5 to 50 cycles per second. The flow round the cylinder was then plotted with and without the oscillatory motion, as contours, and in the latter case the field was found to approximate to what one could obtain

---

* *Loc. cit.*, p. 33.   † *Comptes Rendus*, **224**, 446, 532, 893 (1947).

in one-way motion by increasing the speed of the wind past the model above the critical.

Since these experiments were done, Tollmien* and Schlichting† have examined this synthetic turbulence theoretically and found, for the case of the flat plate, in what gamut of frequency the superposed S.H.M. should lie in order that the amplitude of the disturbance should grow along the plate. (This depends on certain assumptions with regard to the profile of velocity at the surface of the plate and so on the pressure gradient; actually the distribution of p. 30 was taken as starting-point.) For a given Reynolds number, both low and high frequencies should be damped, intermediate ones amplified. Schubauer and Skramstad‡ have recently made similar experiments on plates to those of Richardson and Tyler for pipes and cylinders, using a wind-tunnel carefully protected against

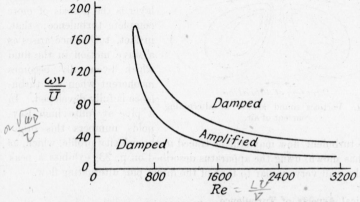

Fig. 30. Régime of stable oscillations in flow along a flat plate.

inherent turbulence, and have confirmed in a general manner these critical regions of frequency as provocators of turbulence (cf. Fig. 30, where the parameter $\omega v/U$ is plotted against Reynolds number).

Another type of periodic boundary layer is associated with a bodily to-and-fro motion of a solid relative to the fluid which surrounds it. Such occurs when an obstacle like a cylinder is stationary in a pipe in which to-and-fro motion of the air particles due to the passage of sound waves is set up. This case has been studied experimentally by Andrade§ and theoretically by Schlichting,|| who starts from equation (23) and puts in the appropriate boundary conditions. Four vortices circulating in four quadrants about the obstacle are set up in the fluid (Fig. 31) where the white dot represents the mean position of a sphere oscillating on the axis.

* Proc. Int. Congress App. Mech., Stockholm, 105 (1930).
† Z. f. ange. Math. u. Mech., 13, 170 (1933).   ‡ J. Aero. Sci. (1947).
§ Proc. Roy. Soc., A134, 445 (1931). || Phys. Zeits., 33, 327 (1932).

On a larger scale, the phenomenon is observed when stationary sound waves are set up in a tube. In this case the relative periodic motion has different amplitudes at different places, being a maximum opposite an antinode and nil at a node. Rayleigh* calculated the shape of the stream-lines for the circulations set up between node and antinode and Andrade,† by photography of smoke particles, has verified that they do take place in close accordance with theory and as shown in Fig. 32. Compare in the same figure the stream-lines in the two half-circuits due to theory (left) and experiment (right).

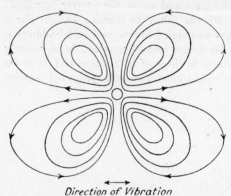

Direction of Vibration

Fig. 31. Vortices round sphere in alternating current of air.

We have hinted at the head of this section that a flow with periodic boundary layer is the genesis of more complete turbulence; that, in fact, turbulence arises as a wave motion in the fluid which eventually becomes incoherent when the turbulence is fully developed. In a pipe at quite high Reynolds numbers this origin of the turbulent flow may still be traced in the velocity profile, which, as Fage has shown, using the apparatus described on p. 33, exhibits a peak near the wall very similar to that of the direct plus alternating flow.

Statistical Aspects of Turbulence

When u, v, w represent the fluctuations in velocity—in the three co-ordinate directions—characteristic of turbulence, Osborne Reynolds

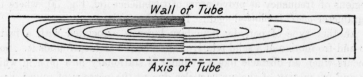

Wall of Tube

Axis of Tube

Fig. 32. Circulations of solid particles in stationary sound waves in air.

expressed the shearing stresses for parallel flow at speed U in the x-direction thus:

$$\tau_{x,\,y}=-\rho\overline{uv}; \quad \tau_{x,\,z}=-\rho\overline{uw} \quad \quad \ldots \quad (33)$$

where the bar indicates that the mean temporal value of the product is to be taken. These formulae indicate that the turbulent flow at a point

* *Phil. Trans.*, **175**, 1 (1883).   † *Ibid.*, **230**, 413 (1932).

is conceived in terms of the magnitude of the components of velocity-fluctuation and the *correlation* between them. From this point of view one regards turbulence in the same fashion that Brownian motion and diffusion are regarded in molecular physics.

The shearing forces in turbulent motion can also be written in terms of a new coefficient of viscosity appropriate to the type of flow called "eddy viscosity," written ν' or A, replacing ν and η respectively in laminar flow, so that we write

$$\tau_{x,\,y} = \rho\nu'\frac{dU}{dy} = A\frac{dU}{dy} \qquad \ldots \ldots \quad (34)$$

in a form similar to that for laminar flow. The coefficient A, which is less often found, has the name *austausch*, due to W. Schmidt.

The dimensions of ν' are of the product of a velocity and a length. It seems appropriate to take v for the velocity in question, since it is the component at right angles to the general flow which is responsible for the diffusion of fluctuations, and a length l, like the mean free path in molecular physics, defined in this wise that particles coming into a given x-plane of flow from mean distances $\pm l$ above or below it are supposed to carry their momentum into it without loss, just as in molecular motion they would carry temperature or density. Having reached the plane they should lose their identity and add the property they carry to the general stock of this stratum. Prandtl* called l the "mixing-length" and it is related to eddy viscosity by the relation

$$\nu' = \overline{v}l$$

Returning to (34) we note that $\overline{v}$ is proportional to the mean velocity difference between fluid masses, i.e. to $l|\partial U/\partial y|$. We take the correlation coefficient between this quantity and v to be unity, i.e. completely linked, and so obtain, with Prandtl:

$$\tau = \rho l^2 \left| \frac{dU}{dy} \right| \frac{dU}{dy} \qquad \ldots \ldots \ldots \quad (35)$$

It may be noted in passing that the form of these equations expresses the law of variation of resistance (of which τ must be a measure) and mean $\overline{U}$. Thus (34) suggests that, provided ν' is constant, $\tau \propto \overline{U}$, while (35) suggests, if l is to be constant, $\tau \propto \overline{U}^2$, as we find for obstacles in a stream. There are, however, many cases in which, though this Newtonian law applies, yet l varies from place to place and with U.

The spreading of a turbulent jet as it emerges from a slit into still air is a good instance of the application of the mixing-length concept. l proves to be proportional to x, the distance along the axis of the jet measured from the orifice. In two-dimensional motion, the equation is, in

* *Z. f. ange Math. u. Mech.*, **5**, 137 (1925).

terms of shearing stress and ultimately of mixing length, by (23) and (35):

$$U\frac{\partial U}{\partial x} + V\frac{\partial U}{\partial y} = -\frac{\partial}{\partial y}\left\{l^2\left(\frac{\partial U}{\partial y}\right)^2\right\}$$

If $l=\kappa x$, $U_{y=0}\propto x^{-1/2}$ and the boundary layer parameter, $\zeta=y/x$. Tollmien* solved the equations with the edge conditions $U=0$, $\partial U/\partial y=0$, and obtained a distribution of U with ζ in agreement with experiment. The quantity of fluid passing through a cross-section of the jet is found to increase as $\sqrt{x}$, the increment being aspirated by the jet from its surroundings.

Taylor† had put forward, some years before Prandtl, another transport theory of turbulence in which "vorticity" was the property conveyed. In two-dimensional motion this leads to an equation similar to (34), but to different quantities for the momentum communicated to unit volume in unit time. This is $\rho\bar{vl}.d^2U/dy^2$ according to Taylor, $\rho.d/dy(\bar{vl}.dU/dy)$ according to Prandtl. There is also a difference in heat transport into the stream (cf. Chap. 4) for which the corresponding temperature distribution is $\theta/\theta_0=\{1-y/y_0)^{3/2}\}$ on the one theory and $\theta/\theta_0=\{1-(y/y_0)^{3/2}\}^2$ on the other. Fage and Falkner‡ have measured the velocity distribution in a wake and find better agreement with the vorticity transport theory. Hall and Hislop§ have measured both velocity and temperature across the wake of a heated body of revolution. Their results, according to Goldstein's‖ analysis, fit the momentum transport theory as well as a modified form of the vorticity transport theory indifferently except at the edges, where there is intimate mixing of the wake with the cold stream. It must be admitted that in many applications of turbulence the difference between the two distributions, on the rival theories, is beyond the limits of accuracy of the measuring technique.

In flow along a flat plate, we can write (35) as

$$\frac{1}{\rho}.\frac{\partial p}{\partial x} = \frac{\partial}{\partial y}\left[l^2\left|\frac{dU}{dy}\right|.\frac{dU}{dy}\right] \quad . \quad . \quad . \quad . \quad (36)$$

There is experimental justification for the assumption that in fully developed turbulence the local velocity gradient and the viscosity have no influence on the shape of the flow; then l can depend on y only, the perpendicular distance from the wall. With this assumption $l=\kappa y$, (35) becomes:

$$\tau = \rho\kappa^2 y^2\left(\frac{dU}{dy}\right)^2 \quad . \quad . \quad . \quad . \quad . \quad (37)$$

remembering that when τ is positive so must be dU/dy.

Integrating (37) for constant τ:

$$U = \frac{U_0}{\kappa}\log_e y + \text{constant} \quad . \quad . \quad . \quad . \quad (38)$$

---

* Z. f. ange. Math. u. Mech., **6**, 468 (1926).   † Phil. Trans., **A215**, 1 (1915).
‡ Proc. Roy. Soc., **A135**, 702 (1932).   § Proc. Camb. Phil. Soc., **34**, 345 (1938).
‖ Ibid., **34**, 351 (1938).

This relation, due to von Kármán,* i.e. that the mean velocity at any level is proportional to the logarithm of its distance from the wall in turbulent flow, is adequately satisfied by the experiments, though it must be admitted that power laws, $U \propto y^n$ (with $n = \frac{1}{7}$, $\frac{1}{8}$, $\frac{1}{9}$), can also fit the results with as good grace.

By assuming that the shear stress across the section of a circular pipe of radius a varies with distance r from the wall according to the relation $\tau = \tau_0 r/a$, Nikuradse† has calculated l from his own plots of U against r across a smooth-walled pipe, applying (36). These are shown in Fig. 33, from which it is apparent that the relationship of l to y ($=a-r$) falls

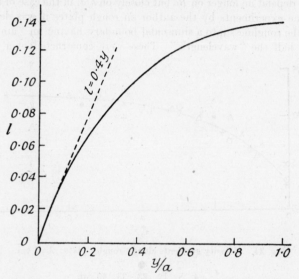

Fig. 33. Variation in mixing-length with distance from wall.

away from simple proportionality (with $\kappa = 0 \cdot 4$) towards the centre of the pipe.

With rough walls similar conditions apply in fully developed turbulence, but y must be reckoned from an arbitrary zero, depending on the scale and type of roughness.

Conditions of similitude demand that in comparing flow over rough surfaces the surfaces be geometrically similar. Experimenters usually attempt to control roughness by sticking uniform grains of sand to the walls or by giving the latter a waviness of specified amplitude and wavelength in the direction of flow, but the undulations, as we have seen, may produce special effects in the transition régime. Both types of model

* Proc. Int. Congress App. Mech., Stockholm, 85 (1930).
† Verh. deut. Ing. Forschungsheft, 356, 21 (1932).

roughness are in any case artificial and do not correspond either to the surface of the ground or to a roughly finished casting. Perhaps the most expressive parameters in which to characterise the roughness are the mean height of the protuberances h and the mean path λ between humps which the fluid encounters, expressed in relation to the distance x along the plate or radius a of the pipe respectively. Of these, the former is more significant, especially if it can be expressed as a fraction of boundary layer thickness δ. Unless the rugosities are of the type to provoke a periodic boundary layer they will be ineffective in the sub-critical region, but after turbulence has supervened, wherever $h > 0.8\delta$ the resistance is found to depend no longer on Re but closely on h/a, in the case of the pipe.

In some experiments by the author on rough plates it was decided to idealise the roughness into a sinusoidal boundary having an "amplitude" equal to half the "wavelength." These were constructed of a series of

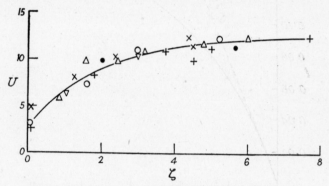

Fig. 34. Velocity gradients along "rough" plate; $\lambda = 1$ cm.
$$x = \begin{array}{cccccc} \times & \bigcirc & + & \bullet & \triangledown & \triangle \\ 4 & 8 & 12 & 23 & 33 & 43 \text{ cm.} \end{array}$$

equi-spaced wires set transversely to the stream, soldered on a plate. Wax was then run on to the plate, and when it had set it was gouged out of the interspaces to the set template. The three constructed had $\lambda = 0.5, 1, 1.6$ cm. respectively, and troughs of depth $\frac{1}{2}\lambda$. The plates were mounted in mid-stream, in a region of (originally) uniform velocity. The velocities in the neighbourhood of the smooth and the two roughest plates are shown on Figs. 19, 34, 35. To conform with the Blasius theory of skin-friction (cf. p. 30), the velocities are plotted against the parameter $\zeta = \sqrt{(Uy^2/x)}$. On Figs. 34 and 35, y is measured from the top of the undulations, which is admittedly an uncertain zero, but the distribution of velocity does show a steeper gradient at this position than does the smooth plate, which gradient does in some measure serve as a criterion of the roughness. The gradients for the three rough plates were in the ratio 4 : 5 : 6, as nearly as could be estimated. The observed distributions satisfy, except very close to the boundary, that postulated by Prandtl, i.e.

$$U = a \log (\zeta + b),$$

where a and b are constants dependent on the roughness, so that the gradient

$$\frac{\partial U}{\partial \zeta} = \frac{a}{\zeta + b}$$

Turbulence can also be described in terms of the distribution of amplitude and frequency in what is often called the "spectrum" of the fluctuations. As regards the first of these factors it is usual to express the results in terms of u/U, v/U, and w/U and to call this the scale of turbulence. If the three values are equal the turbulence is "isotropic."

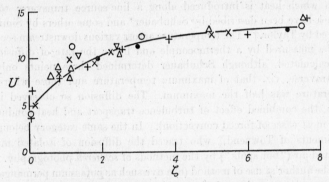

Fig. 35. Velocity gradients "along" rough plate; $\lambda = 1\cdot6$ cm.

. Turbulent mixing may be considered as a problem in the diffusion of a quantity c (momentum or vorticity) and governed by Fick's law

$$\frac{\partial c}{\partial t} = v' \frac{\partial^2 c}{\partial y^2} \qquad \dots \qquad \dots \qquad (39)$$

where v' takes the place of the coefficient of diffusion in molecular diffusion. Equation (39) may be applied in a number of boundary conditions pertaining to the shape of the source of diffusion and the manner of its maintenance. Thus if the source of diffusion covers a line perpendicular to the flow at mean speed U and with a constant value of v'—no dissipation of energy into heat—

$$c = \frac{c_0}{2\sqrt{(\pi v' t)}} e^{-y^2/4v't}$$

c_0 being the maintained "concentration" at $y = 0$; or writing $\overline{Y^2}$ for $2v't$:

$$c = \frac{c_0}{\sqrt{(2\pi \overline{Y^2})}} e^{-y^2/2\overline{Y^2}} \qquad \dots \qquad \dots \qquad (40)$$

$\overline{Y^2}$ represents the mean square of the vertical distance diffused from the horizontal plane through the source.

The form of this equation is that of the Gaussian error-function and gives the distribution of momentum (or other property) about the maximum value at any co-ordinate. The spectrum of turbulent frequencies is similarly distributed about the maximum frequency.

The general principle of diffusion measurements requires the introduction into the fluid of some material or energy whose subsequent distribution can be determined by the analysis of instrumental records. If energy be introduced it may take the form of (a) an inexorable oscillation of fixed frequency and amplitude, or (b) a constant supply of heat. If mass transport is to be studied the source may take the form of (c) colour or (d) a solid such as smoke, dust, or silt.

Method (a) has been already mentioned (p. 40.) Experiments of class (b), in which heat is introduced along a line-source transverse to the channel, have been described by Schubauer* and some others by Simmons are cited by Taylor.† The temperature across various downstream sections may be measured by a thermocouple and hence the rate of diffusion of heat calculated, although Schubauer determined three points only on each traverse, viz. that of maximum temperature and those where the temperature was half the maximum. The diffusion so observed is, of course, the combined effect of turbulence-transport and heat-conduction (as in most cases of forced convection). In the same category belong the experiments of Townend,‡ who traced the diffusion of isolated masses of heated air ("hot spots") by the methods of *schlieren* photography.

In the author's§ use of method (c) a dye such as potassium permanganate is let into a water channel along a horizontal line perpendicular to the direction of flow. The dye dissolves and is diffused downstream by the intermingling of the fluid passing the "source" with neighbouring strata, and the time-average of the colour-density at any level (x, y) is measured by a horizontal beam of light traversing the channel and falling upon a photo-electric cell. At first the dye was introduced by siphoning a concentrated solution through a narrow tube, mounted transversely to the stream and pierced at the after edge with a number of small holes. It was found that the tube tended to induce turbulence in its wake. Further, any velocity relative to the main stream which the jets might have on emergence was a disturbing factor. Latterly a thin phosphor-bronze strip was stretched tightly across the stream and this, painted with a soluble gum and the finely powdered solid dye, acted as the line source. Several seconds elapsed before the gum was dissolved off and the dye began to colour the stream, so that the fitting of the source in position was not accompanied by a vivid overall coloration of the stream such as resulted when the powder was directly applied to the strip.

* *Rep. N.A.C.A.*, 524 (1935).   † *Proc. Roy. Soc.*, **A151**, 421 (1935).
‡ *Proc. Roy. Soc.*, **A145**, 180 (1934).   § *Proc. Phys. Soc.*, **49**, 484 (1937).

A water channel with a 2-h.p. circulating pump was available, which permitted speeds of 20 cm. per second, corresponding to a Reynolds number of 60,000. The difficulty now was that the water reintroduced upstream into the channel was contaminated by the dye and tinted before it reached the grating. This was overcome by making the water slightly acid and bubbling sulphur dioxide into the pump intake, to "reduce" the permanganate at the correct rate so that the water was returned colourless to the channel. An auxiliary fixed beam of light was sent athwart the channel to another photo-electric cell upstream of the model, and the out-of-balance current between the two photo-electric cells read on a Wheatstone bridge in which the cells formed one pair of ratio arms.

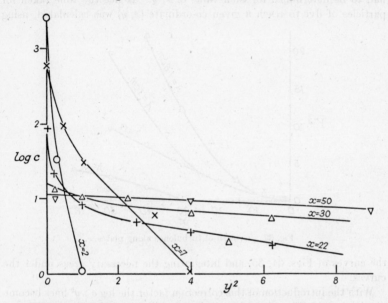

Fig. 36.   Diffusion of turbulence along "rough" plate; $\lambda = 1$ cm.

With this compensating device it did not matter if the reduction of the permanganate was not quite complete on the return of the water to the channel. It should be added that the channel was given sufficient slope to produce "uniform flow" as estimated by traversing a hot-wire anemometer across the experimental section.

The distribution of the dye in any vertical plane will be given by (40) and $\overline{Y^2}$ by the negative slope of the graph of y^2 against $\log c$. This method was applied to the plates aforementioned with the source stretched along the leading edge (Fig. 36). Measurements of the concentration of the dye in various planes perpendicular to the plate and distances (x) from the leading edge were made, but before being plotted as $\log c : y^2$ curves, a correction had to be made for the gradient of U near the surface of the plate. In consequence of this velocity gradient the diffusion appears more rapid at first as the dye leaves the plate. In actual fact, the concentrations recorded at small values of y represent a proportionately higher value of t than those for larger y at the same value of x. It will appear that the scattering velocity v in the direction perpendicular to the plate is nearly constant, whereas the "drift velocity" parallel to the plate increases outwards, and the average velocity

$$\overline{U}=\frac{1}{\zeta}\int_0^{\zeta} U d\zeta$$

had to be determined for each value of x, y. Hence the time taken for particles of dye to reach a given co-ordinate (x, y) was calculated, using

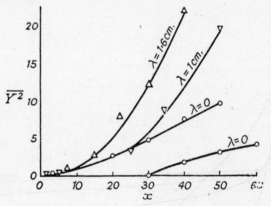

Fig. 37.   Growth of turbulence along plates.

the curves of Figs. 34, 35, and integrating the necessary areas under the curves.

With the introduction of this correction factor the log c : y^2 lines become nearly straight (Fig. 36), although there is still a tendency for the diffusion velocity to increase in the first few millimetres from the plate as well as with time. The former increase may be accounted for by an hypothesis that the vortices originate from a level slightly above the level of the plate or of the crests on it. The latter increase is brought out by the $\overline{Y^2}$: x curves (Fig. 37) which indicate that vorticity is added to the stream by its passage over the plate, particularly by the rough plates, for which a rapid increase of slope of the $\overline{Y^2}$: x line occurs as the stern is approached. This rate is roughly proportional to λ. The short, smooth plate shows a less rapid growth, with the usual dissipation occurring beyond the stern (decreasing slope). The importance of the parameter ζ can be shown in these diffusion measurements as well as in relation to velocity gradients, for it is possible to reduce all the measurements for a given plate to a single curve by plotting them against ζ^{-2}. In Fig. 38 this has been done for the smooth plate.

Correlations in Turbulent Motion

G. I. Taylor* introduced the idea of "diffusion by continuous movement" in which the process is not limited to finite steps—"mixing lengths"— or to finite intervals of time. This concept involves the idea of a correlation between the position, momentum, or other physical property of a particle at a place A and that which it has when it gets to B, or between the simultaneous values of the property which two particles at A and B

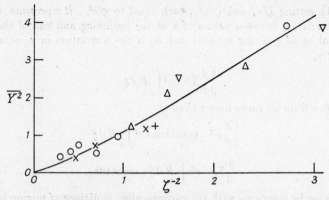

Fig. 38. Growth of turbulence along plate.

possess. Thus, if momentum is the property in question, the coefficient of correlation is defined as:

$$R = \frac{u_A \cdot u_B}{\sqrt{(u_A^2)} \cdot \sqrt{(u_B^2)}} \quad \cdots \cdots \quad (41)$$

when A and B are two points on the x axis, or when they are on the y axis and observations of u_A, u_B are made at the the same instant. When A and B are close together R is nearly unity but tends to zero (no relationship) when they are taken far apart.

We can usefully picture this in terms of the sizes of the eddies which drift with the stream, like puffs of smoke in the atmosphere. If the stations A and B happen to lie closer together than the diameter of the eddies on the average, we shall expect a close relationship between the events at the two stations, just as if they were on opposite sides of a stationary vortex; contrariwise, when the eddies are small compared to the distance AB.

* Proc. Roy. Soc., **A151**, 429 (1935).

If in vertical diffusion across a horizontal current a particle reaches a level Y in a time t, $Y = \int_0^t v \, dt$ and

$$\frac{1}{2} \frac{d}{dt} \overline{Y^2} = Y \frac{\overline{dY}}{dt} = \overline{Y v_t} = v_t \overline{\int_0^t v \, dt}$$

the suffix denoting a particular instant of time. If the time in the integral is divided into n intervals, the contribution of the jth interval, at the beginning and end of which v has values v_j and v_{j+1} respectively, to the average is

$$\frac{t}{n} \overline{v_j \cdot v_{j+1}} = \frac{t}{n} \overline{v^2} R,$$

by (41), setting $\sqrt{v_j{}^2}$ and $\sqrt{v_j{}^2_{+1}}$ each equal to $\sqrt{v^2}$. R represents, then, the correlation between values of v at the beginning and end of the jth interval or, if ξ is this interval and R_ξ is the correlation in v, over the time t/n,

$$\frac{1}{2} \frac{d}{dt} \overline{Y^2} = \overline{v^2} \int_0^t R_\xi \, d\xi$$

If $R_\xi = 0$ for all times longer than t_1,

$$\frac{1}{2} \frac{d}{dt} \overline{Y^2} = \text{constant} \times \overline{v^2} \int_0^t R_\xi \, d\xi$$

$$\frac{1}{2} \overline{Y^2} = \overline{v^2} t \int_0^t R_\xi \, d\xi + \text{constant} \quad \ldots \quad (42)$$

This may be compared with the corresponding equations of mixing length theories if

$$l = \overline{v} \int_0^{t_1} R_\xi \, d\xi$$

When t is small,

$$R_\xi = 1 \quad \text{and} \quad \overline{Y^2} = \overline{v^2} t_1{}^2$$

so that near the source

$$\sqrt{(\overline{Y^2})} = \overline{v} t = \frac{\overline{v} x}{U}$$

If there is dissipation of turbulent energy this will be shown by the form of the departure from completely linked correlation as the time goes on or distance increases. (Such dissipation is often shown first as a breaking up of large into small vortices.) A length λ can be defined by the equation

$$\frac{1}{\lambda^2} = L_{y \to 0} \frac{1 - R_y}{y^2}$$

A curve of R_y against y will, by this reasoning, be a parabola in the absence of dissipation; otherwise λ is the intercept on the axis of y of a parabola drawn to touch the curve at the vertex (cf. Fig. 41).

Measurement of Correlation in Turbulence

In the method adopted by the author* the fluctuations at any point in a fluid are measured by letting a dye into the fluid from a capillary tube a little upstream from the observation station, at which a fine beam of light passes athwart the stream to fall on a photo-electric cell. Fluctuations in magnitude or direction of the stream at the station will cause changes in the local concentration of the dye, and these, in turn, will cause variations in the light falling on the cell and so in the photo-electric current. The experiments to be described were carried out in a water channel 6 ft. long and 10 in. wide, and the maximum depth of water was 1 ft.

It was, of course, necessary to establish a relation between the colour-density of the diffusing dye and the photo-electric current in the cell when it was illuminated by a horizontal beam of light interrupted by the colour. The voltage at which the photo-electric cell gave a linear response to intensity of illumination was first found by trial, then a small portion of the channel was sealed off to form a tank into which solutions of known concentration of the dye were introduced in turn, and the response of the cell to light passing through the solution was measured. It was found that, over the normal range of colour-density in the subsequent experiments, a linear relation existed between the concentration and the current-defect, i.e. the difference between the reading of the galvanometer with clear water and that with the dye in solution. The clear water reading was maintained constant during the experiments by adjusting the width of the beam whenever necessary. By an arrangement of gears and rails the photo-electric cell and its associated beam of light could be traversed in the x, y plane through the water without losing their orientation.

In adapting the optical method to the measurement of correlations in the turbulence in the channel one proceeds as follows. A thin glass tube lets in dye from an orifice pointing downstream at the point A, and at the same point a pencil of light crosses the channel horizontally to one of a pair of matched photo-electric cells. A similar arrangement suffices for a point B with the second photo-cell, except that the whole of this duplicate device can be racked up and down without alteration of the relative positions of lamp, orifice, and photo-cell. Thus while A is a fixed station in the channel, B can lie at any height above A or at a place on the same horizontal level further down the stream. The two photo-cells were connected with two variable high resistances, a rectifier connected to a galvanometer and a high-tension battery to form a Wheatstone bridge (Fig. 39b), the idea being that as long as the march of events occurred at B in step with those at A no current would pass through the rectifier, but as the correlation between fluctuations at A and B became less, an increasing, but of course alternating, current would pass through the rectifier, and in consequence the mean deflection of the galvanometer would

* *Proc. Phys. Soc.*, **49**, 488 (1937).

increase. To indicate the relation between this deflection and the correlation, and in some measure to act as a calibration of the optical apparatus, it was removed from the channel and the light beams arranged to pass near the circumference of a disc which could be rotated at speed. The circumference of the disc was cut in the shape of an epicycloid with two cusps. When the two beams and cells were mounted at opposite ends of a diameter while the disc was revolved, the light on each cell varied in simple harmonic fashion but in phase, so that no current was recorded on the galvanometer. One cell being fixed, the other, with its consort beam, was moved slowly round the circumference of the disc, the deflection of the galvanometer increasing as the light fluctuations got out of step until at a phase difference of π (corresponding to an angular separation of the cells equal to $\pi/2$) the deflection reached a maximum, to fall again as the cells approached each other round the circumference. If one substitutes in the expression (41) for the correlation coefficients two S.H.Ms.

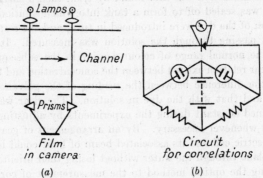

Fig. 39. Apparatus and circuit for measuring correlations in turbulence.

of equal amplitude and frequency but phase difference δ, the expression reduces to cos δ. Approximate proportionality between galvanometer deflection and the cosine of the phase difference is indicated by the calibration results (Fig. 40). Accordingly it was assumed that when the device was applied to a stream in the manner indicated, the deflection of the rectifier-galvanometer would measure the correlation coefficient directly, with the help of this calibration curve.

The two correlations, one across the stream and one downstream, with one beam at a fixed station 9 in. behind a $\frac{3}{8}$-in. grating, are shown by the continuous lines in Fig. 41. As G. I. Taylor indicates from theoretical considerations, the correlation with x falls off more slowly than that with y, though the type of correlation here measured is not quite the same as that envisaged by Taylor, since the measurements are concerned with the relative phase as well as the magnitude of the fluctuations.

Another type of correlation can be investigated by comparing the oscillation at station A with that at B on the same level further downstream, after allowing sufficient time to elapse for the general current to carry a pulsation at A down to B. A length of photographic film must then intervene between the records of the respective fluctuations. The two beams of light after passing perpendicularly across the stream were inclined by small-angled prisms until focused side by side on the film in continuous movement through a camera at a known speed. (A single wide beam was used when x was less than 2 cm.) The dye caused oscillations in the intensity of the light, revealed as variations in the blackness of the film on development. The film was then passed again through the light beams and cells, one for each half of the film connected in the circuit of Fig. 39, but the pick-up for B was proportionately lower down the film than for A—somewhat after the fashion in which the light and sound tracks are picked up from a talking film—so that the galvanometer deflection measured the correlation between A and B after the proper time interval had elapsed. This correlation is shown by the dotted line

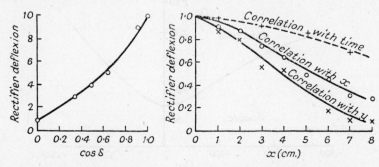

Fig. 40. Calibration curve
for correlations.

Fig. 41. Correlations in turbulence
induced by grating.

on Fig. 41. In the absence of dissipation a disturbance would be conveyed with unchanged amplitude down the channel, but in fact the correlation gradually departs from unity as time goes on.

The more usual, and probably more accurate, method of measuring correlations involves the use of two hot wires and is described on p. 83.

These correlation coefficients are, as we have observed, closely related to the mean diameters of the vortices which often are the cause of the fluctuations. On p. 26 and in Figs. 13, 14 we have seen how the correlation between the currents in two hot wires in a wake can be used to measure the inter-spacing of vortices. The same arrangement can be used in more generally turbulent régimes for measuring mean eddy diameter. As one wire is moved from the other, first the amplitude of the induced currents in the secondary of the transformer will decrease and then increase again if there is any preferred distance in the flow pattern corresponding to a prevalent vortex spacing or core width, but if the fluctuations are quite incoherent no such preferred distance will be found (cf. Chap. 4).

Stability of Flow

We have already referred to instability in a boundary layer as a common genesis of turbulence. Consider the case of two concentric cylinders enclosing a layer of fluid. When the outer cylinder rotates faster than the inner one, the distribution of centrifugal forces is such as to stabilise the motion of the fluid, but if the inner one is rotating faster, the opposite is the case. The ratio of the critical speeds in the two cases is about 6 to 1. G. I. Taylor* has predicted and confirmed by experiment that when laminar flow breaks down, the interspace divides into compartments in which ring-shaped vortices are set up. These vortices embrace the inner cylinder and rotate about their ring-shaped cores like the vortex rings

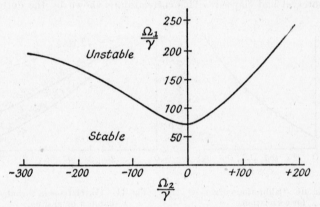

Fig. 42. Stability in flow between coaxial cylinders; radii 3·55 and 4·035 cm.

formed by tobacco smoke. It is true that this is not exactly turbulence as we generally understand it, since the pattern is regular and stationary, but it is yet another intermediate stage of a periodic nature between stream-line and turbulent motion. The importance of Taylor's theoretical investigation lies in the fact that it is one of the very few problems to which the complete Navier–Stokes equations have been applied with beautiful experimental confirmation. Fig. 42 shows the theoretical and experimental regions of stability and instability for various values of Ω_1 and Ω_2; these being the angular velocities of the inner and outer cylinders respectively.

Curvature of the boundary has, then, a marked influence on stability. So, too, with flow in a channel has the relative curvature of the walls, i.e whether the channel is convergent or divergent, the former favouring

* *Phil. Trans.*, **A223**, 280 (1923).

stability, the latter opposing it. A more important factor is the pressure gradient, an accelerating gradient delaying transition, pushing the critical value of Reynolds number in the boundary layer to higher values.

The final factor in stability to which we shall refer is a density gradient. If there is a thin layer of fluid between two horizontal flat plates and the upper plate is hotter than the lower, very little motion of the fluid will take place since the warmer layers are at the top, but if the lower is the hotter, unstable thermal currents supervene which also divide up the

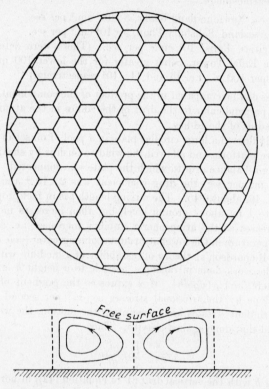

Fig. 43.   Bénard cells in fluid stratum having a density gradient.

space into regular cell-like vortices. Inside these rotary motion takes place in the form of miniature convection currents. Bénard* first demonstrated them in a film of collodion between two glass plates close together, but the same phenomenon is believed to be the origin on a huge scale of the cellular clouds which sometimes divide up the sky into a pattern of chequers. Fig. 43 shows Bénard's vortices in plan and in section.

* *Ann. de chim. et phys.*, **33**, 62 (1901).

Atmospheric Turbulence

These considerations apply with special significance to the atmosphere and the way in which turbulence on a large scale may originate in it. Similar remarks apply to the oceans.

Values of the eddy-viscosity ν' can be determined from the distribution of momentum (i.e. wind speed or water speed) with height, or, in the ocean, of salinity with height. G. I. Taylor[*] deduced the following values of ν' for the atmosphere:

(a) over sea, Newfoundland banks, 3×10^3 cm.^{2} per sec.

(b) over grassland, Salisbury Plain, 5×10^4 cm.^{2} per sec.

(c) over cities, Paris, 10^5 cm.^{2} per sec. (These were determined on the Eiffel Tower, being greater for the lower 100 m. than the upper 100 m., i.e. 15 and 11×10^4 respectively.)

These values can be compared to the product of the component of velocity fluctuation perpendicular to the drift of the eddies in the atmosphere and the mean radius of the eddies.

Sheppard[†] floated a large circular plate in a pool of oil set in the middle of a concrete platform and allowed the wind to push it by shearing action, so deflecting a balance arm to which the plate was connected. At a wind speed of 4 m. per sec. the drag coefficient was 2×10^{-3} and the factor κ of (37), p. 46, about 0·45. The mixing length l is in fact proportional to height up to 1 m. above ground level, but then increases more rapidly. κ also decreases as the atmospheric stability increases, i.e. as the lapse rate of temperature in the lower stratum becomes greater (*vide infra*).

In L. F. Richardson's[‡] theory of instability of a medium with a density gradient, the work done in raising a particle to a height h is equated to $\frac{1}{2}\rho g \beta h^2$, where $\beta = 1/\rho \,|\, d\rho/dh\,|$. If α expresses the gradient of U with h, the work done by the frictional stresses is $|\tau\alpha|$ per second (cf. p. 45). If these turbulent stresses are to maintain the motion, the work they do must exceed that done against gravity. Then

$$|\tau\alpha| > \frac{1}{2}\rho g \beta \frac{d}{dt}(\overline{h^2}) \quad\quad\quad\quad (43)$$

Identifying h with the vertical drift (Y of equation (42)) in horizontal flow at speed U, we can write

$$\frac{1}{2}\frac{d}{dt}(\overline{h^2}) = \overline{vl} \quad\quad\quad\quad (44)$$

and from the momentum transported:

$$\tau = \rho\overline{vl}\alpha \quad\quad\quad\quad (45)$$

so that for maintenance of turbulence, L. F. Richardson's number $\alpha^2/g\beta$ must be greater than 1; *per contra*, if this parameter is less than 1, the

[*] *Rep. du Con. Intern. pour l'Exploration de la mer*, **76**, 35 (1931).
[†] *Proc. Roy. Soc.*, **A188**, 268 (1947).   [‡] *Phil. Trans.*, **A97**, 354 (1920).

flow is non-turbulent or stable.   Taylor has further calculated that for
the stability of an inviscid fluid with a uniform and small density gradient
in uniform shear, the parameter must be less than 4.

[The parameter can also be expressed in terms of the gradient of temperature with height ("lapse rate") for

$$\frac{a^2}{g/\rho \cdot d\rho/dh} = \frac{(dU/dh)^2}{g/\theta \cdot \{d\theta/dh - (d\theta/dh)_0\}}$$

where $(d\theta/dh)_0$ is the "adiabatic lapse rate" such that air moving from
lower to upper levels finds itself in temperature equilibrium with its new
surroundings after the loss of temperature that it undergoes due to internal
expansion, so that no exchange of heat takes place.]

The critical value is found in practice to depend on the Reynolds
number of the motion, and since mixing between layers of different
density is involved it is possible that a third parameter—Froude number,

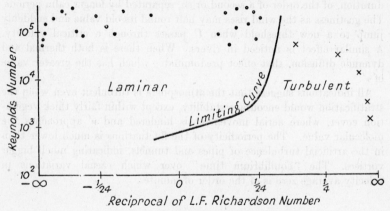

Fig. 44.   Atmospheric stability criteria.

cf. Chap. 5—must be reckoned with.   Fig. 44 (after Paeschke*) shows,
by dots, the values of Re at which atmospheric instability has been
observed to set in.   Turbulence *may* be set up at any value of density
gradient, but when the Richardson number is less than 4 it occurs more
readily, i.e. at lower Reynolds numbers.

Experimental results on a large scale are wanting for the atmosphere,
but hydrographic measurements of ocean currents and salinity examined
by Jacobsen† show that turbulence can subsist in the ocean with $a^2/g\beta$
as small as 0·008.   On the other hand, Sverdrup,‡ who has examined data
over a wider field, thinks that the momentum transport theory is adequate
to explain the observed facts, having regard to the difficulty in collecting
and assessing the data.

* *Beit. z. Phys. d. Atmos.*, **24**, 163 (1937).   † *Beit. z. Geophys.*, **16**, 404 (1927).
‡ *Geofysk. Pub.*, No. 7 (1936).

Wind Structure

It is found that the mean wind varies with height according to a rule $U \propto h^j$, though this seems uncertain in its application near the ground. The principal variations of j are caused by temperature gradients and the "roughness" of the ground, being smaller over broken terrain. Experiments suggest for j a mean value of 0·17 up to 30 m.

Both u and v increase with mean speed and approach equality at heights, but in the first 2 m., v increases more rapidly than w decreases. Even at low wind speeds near the ground gustiness as expressed by the means $\bar{u}$, $\bar{v}$, and $\bar{w}$ may be considerable when the sun's radiation sets up convection currents. Some meteorologists maintain that u/U increases with U at first, but becomes constant when the latter reaches 6 m. per sec. This type of turbulence may be distinguished from simple momentum transport by the fact that it occurs in "quanta," isolated bursts of short duration, of the order of a second or so, separated by longer calm periods. The gustiness as the wind rises may halt round its old value and suddenly jump to a new threshold when U passes through a critical velocity. A similar effect is noticed in rivers. When there is both thermal and dynamic diffusion, that effect predominates which has the greater value of ν'.

All indications suggest that the atmosphere is turbulent even when the stratification would encourage stability, except within fairly thick vegetation cover, where aerial movement is hindered and ν' approaches the molecular value. The periodicity of the fluctuations is much lower than in the artificial turbulence of pipes and tunnels, indicating much bigger vortices. The "equilibrium time" over which casual variations in velocity average zero is of the order of minutes.

CHAPTER 3

THE FLOW OF COMPRESSIBLE FLUIDS

When we are dealing with compressible fluids it is no longer a matter of indifference whether we speak of the volume or the mass of an element. The equation of continuity has to be modified to allow for density changes, thus:

$$\frac{d\rho}{dt}=-\rho\left(\frac{\partial U}{\partial x}+\frac{\partial V}{\partial y}+\frac{\partial W}{\partial z}\right)=-\rho \ \ \text{div}.\,U \quad . \ . \ \ (46)$$

The Bernoulli equation has also to be modified. The general equation for the change of density of a gas between two states 1 and 2 is, in an adiabatic change (i.e. no heat exchange with the surroundings):

$$\int_1^2\frac{dp}{\rho}=\frac{\gamma}{\gamma-1}\frac{p_1}{\rho_1}\left[\left(\frac{\rho_2}{\rho_1}\right)^{\gamma-1}-1\right]$$

γ being the ratio of specific heats at constant pressure c_p and constant volume c_v for then, as is shown in textbooks of thermodynamics,

$$\frac{p_1}{p_2}=\left(\frac{\rho_1}{\rho_2}\right)^{\gamma}$$

if the adiabatic change is frictionless and so reversible. So

$$\frac{1}{2}(U_2{}^2-U_1{}^2)=\frac{a^2}{\gamma-1}\left[\left(\frac{\rho_1}{\rho_2}\right)^{\gamma-1}-1\right] \quad . \ . \ . \ . \ (47)$$

an equation which has wide application to the flow of gases.

[Here a is the adiabatic velocity of sound:

$$a^2=\frac{dp}{d\rho}=\gamma\frac{p}{\rho} \ . \quad . \ . \ . \ . \ . \ . \ (48)]$$

When friction enters, the adiabatic relation is only approximately fulfilled due to the irreversible heat exit. In terms of the values of the corresponding quantities when the fluid is at rest (indicated by zero suffixes),

$$\rho=\rho_0\left[1-\frac{\gamma-1}{2}\frac{U^2}{a_0{}^2}\right]^{1/\gamma-1}$$

$$p=p_0\left[1-\frac{\gamma-1}{2}\frac{U^2}{a_0{}^2}\right]^{\gamma/\gamma-1}$$

$$a^2=a_0{}^2\left[1-\frac{\gamma-1}{2}\frac{U^2}{a_0{}^2}\right] \quad . \ . \ . \ . \ (49)$$

The final equation shows that as the velocity U of the fluid increases it reaches a limit $a_0\sqrt{[2/(\gamma-1)]}$ and that wherever $U=a_0\sqrt{[2/(\gamma+1)]}$, $U=a$. The velocity of the fluid at such a point is then equal to the local velocity of sound. Velocities between this value and the upper limit are known as supersonic.

The motion of a body through a compressible gas at low speeds can nevertheless be described without reference to compressibility, for local compressions and rarefactions which may be produced are not intense and are reversible, but at high speeds precipitate and irreversible changes of density are produced, particularly in the neighbourhood of sharp points and corners. From such places shock waves travel out into the medium. The setting up of what are effectively sound waves involves an additional "wave resistance" as the process transports momentum from the neighbourhood of the obstacle to a distance and converts kinetic energy into heat. Bodies, such as meteors, travelling through the air at high speeds may experience a large temperature rise from this and the ordinary frictional resistance in spite of the loss of heat they suffer from being bathed in a cold atmosphere.

To characterise a potential flow in a compressible medium, we write for the three component velocities,

$$U+u=U+\frac{\partial\phi}{\partial x}; \quad v=\frac{\partial\phi}{\partial y}; \quad w=\frac{\partial\phi}{\partial z}$$

where u, v, w are small compared to U, as in Oseen's approximation (cf. p. 13), but U may be comparable with a. The potential then approximately satisfies the equation

$$a^2\nabla^2\phi=U^2\frac{\partial^2\phi}{\partial x^2}$$

or
$$\left(1-\frac{U^2}{a^2}\right)\frac{\partial^2\phi}{\partial x^2}+\frac{\partial^2\phi}{\partial y^2}+\frac{\partial^2\phi}{\partial z^2}=0 \quad . \quad . \quad . \quad . \quad (50)$$

This reduces to the ordinary potential flow if we substitute x_1 for $x/\sqrt{(1-U^2/a^2)}$ in the régime where $U<a$. In this way the equation of compressible potential flow can be "linearised" into a type of incompressible flow. It is also possible to linearise it into an ordinary sound wave equation (vide infra). The original equations are, of course, relevant to a medium in which both steady motion and wave-making are taking place. [As a matter of general interest, the reader may care to note that the linearisation process in (50) involves two velocities in the same way as in the relativity equations, wherein the so-called Fitzgerald transformation embodies a particle velocity and the velocity of light in vacuo in the same fashion; the latter, however, is a ne plus ultra, whereas the velocity of sound is not.]

The solution of (50) for two-dimensional flow is

$$\phi=\phi_1(x-\alpha y)+\phi_2(x+\alpha y) \quad . \quad . \quad . \quad . \quad (51)$$

where α represents the transformation $\sqrt{[(U^2/a^2)-1]}$ and a is supposed constant all over the field. The lines $x-\alpha y$ and $x+\alpha y=$constant are envelopes to the wave fronts and make an angle 2β together where $\beta = \cot^{-1}\alpha$.

This transformation means that we can start with the ordinary low-speed potential field and contract the stream-lines in the direction of flow in the ratio $1 : \sqrt{(1 - U^2/a^2)}$ to get the flow round the same model in the transonic range, provided the obstacle is so slender that the components v, w which it sets up are small compared to the forward speed U. Practical bodies for high-speed flow are, in fact, of this shape.

G. I. Taylor* originated an ingenious method for solving cases of compressible flow past such bodies by an adaptation of the electrostatic tank which we have already described in relation to incompressible flow (p. 11). Instead of uniform depth of electrolyte the bottom is fashioned to make the depth vary in a predetermined way. If E is the potential and H the flux,

$$\frac{1}{\sigma} \cdot \frac{\partial E}{\partial x} = -f; \quad \frac{1}{\sigma} \frac{\partial E}{\partial y} = -g; \quad \frac{H}{\partial y} = -tf; \quad \frac{H}{\partial x} = tg \quad . \quad . \quad (52)$$

where f, g are the components of electric current density and σ is the specific resistance of the electrolyte of depth t at a given place. By comparing these with the equations for u and v it is evident that we can determine the distribution of ϕ from that of E, if t is made proportional to ρ and a model of the obstacle is made in insulating material.

(Alternatively, the model may be formed in conducting material, E identified with ψ and t made inversely proportional to ρ. The bottom is moulded by trial, starting with constant depth, and in each step taking the E distribution of the previous one as a guide to the depth formation for the next.)

The shock waves spreading from the nose and tail of a bullet were first photographed by Mach† in virtue of the fact that the compression of the air along their envelopes is sufficient to cast an optical shadow on the plate (cf. Fig. 45, Plate I). β is called the Mach angle and U/a the Mach number, M.

The latter is an additional parameter which, together with Reynolds number, must be reckoned with in delineating variations of body resistance. As the speed of the body approaches that of sound locally, the pressure gradient along the surface is altered and so is the point of breakaway which regulates the wake. It is also evident that the surface of the obstacle must be aerodynamically clean, i.e. free from protuberances, if its resistance at sonic and supersonic speeds is not to be excessive. Fig. 46 shows how the drag coefficients of cylinders and spheres vary in this region (ignoring the effect of Reynolds number, which is, however, yet significant) and Fig. 47 the distribution of pressure round a circular cylinder at various Mach numbers (cf. Fig. 16, p. 28).

* (with C. F. Sharman) *Proc. Roy. Soc.*, **A121**, 194 (1928).
† *Wien. Ber.*, **98**, 1310 (1889).

In von Kármán's* acoustic analogy he considers the length $x/\sqrt{(1-U^2/a^2)}$ as a time co-ordinate in the history of a two-dimensional flow taking place as a result of the output of a line of oscillators spaced along the projection of the plan form of the model, located with its axis parallel to the x axis, on to the y, z plane. Each oscillator is supposed to give out a pulse of sound whose intensity distribution in time replaces the thickness distribution in space of the corresponding section of the model. The pulse is then analysed by the Fourier method and from the analysis the drag of the model emerges as the energy transmitted to infinity by all the oscillators during the lifetime of their activity. On this theory, it should be possible to reduce drag in the supersonic régime by suitable interference—in the acoustic sense—between the oscillators. This could

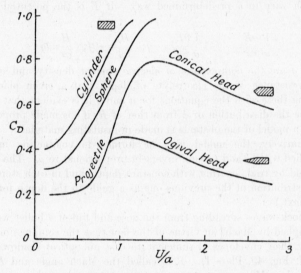

Fig. 46.   Drag coefficients at supersonic speeds.

be, and is in fact, accomplished by sweeping back the model section from its central point—like the pair of wings of some birds—so that, in the acoustic analogy, the representative oscillators start and finish their emission progressively later than the one which stands for the central section.

The linearisation process—whether performed on a purely hydro-dynamic or on an acoustic basis—is only valid for small motions relative to the main flow. If the known variation of the velocity of sound with temperature and displacement amplitude are taken into account, together with the possibility of local speeds not small compared to the main stream or the sound velocity, the equations—such as (50)—are no longer linear.

* J. Aero. Sci., **14**, 373 (1947).

The few Mach cones which cover the whole field in the simpler flow are replaced by many local Mach cones corresponding each to the local velocity of sound and having an axis parallel to the local U and amplitude proportional to the local U/a.

Shock Waves

When the fluid passes through a shock front its speed is suddenly reduced while its pressure and temperature are as suddenly increased. These quantities are connected by the equations of continuity and by an "equation of state," viz. an expression relating pressure, volume, and

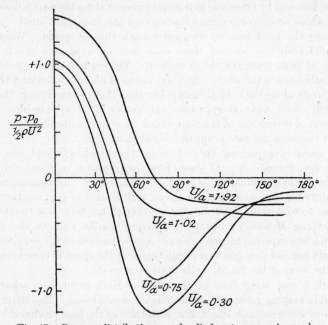

Fig. 47. Pressure distribution round cylinder at supersonic speeds.

temperature. Continuity says that the ratio U/e of velocity to specific volume must remain the same, also

$$e\delta p = U\delta U$$

while for the energy balance:

$$c_v\theta + pe + \frac{U}{2} = \text{constant}$$

From these three expressions, Hugoniot* derived a law connecting the specific volumes and pressures before and after the shock:

$$\frac{e_1}{e_2} = \frac{(\gamma-1)p_2 + (\gamma+1)p_1}{(\gamma-1)p_1 + (\gamma+1)p_2}$$

* J. École. Poly., **57-59** (1887-9).

which has a maximum value of $(\gamma+1)/(\gamma-1)$ for the most intense shocks whereas in a truly adiabatic change there is no such limit.

When a projectile of the usual shape—cone or ogive for head and cylinder for body—is travelling at high speed, these shock waves spread from the vertex in such a fashion that the fluid behind them flows parallel to the diverging sides. Where the sides diverge less or become parallel a progressive expansion takes place while the fluid "turns the corner"— like a squad of soldiers changing front—until it takes on a new direction parallel to the slant sides of the projectile. When the projectile is travelling at a high Mach number, a conical shock wave originates at the vertex, followed by other waves from roughnesses along the slant sides of the head, whose sections are curves leading into the main wave-front. Along the cone the local velocity is greater than that of sound. When the "parallel body" is reached these cease and an expansion occurs with change of front until the tail is reached. There a new dilatation follows with turbulence in the wake. At lower values of M, but still greater than 1, the velocity along the conical body is less than that of sound; only the first (conical) shock wave is apparent. At values of M approaching unity the point of divergence of the main shock wave moves ahead of the vertex and at the same time its projection becomes curved.

At speeds approaching that of sound the breakaway and transition points are affected. Fig. 47 shows how the transition represented by the pressure trough gradually disappears as M increases. In consequence of this, distributions such as those shown will depend in part on Reynolds number as well as on Mach number. Ackeret* has been able to alter the Re, keeping M nearly constant, by having flexible walls to the tunnel in which the experiments were done. As we shall see in the next section, to retain parallel flow in a supersonic tunnel as the speed is varied requires that the form of the tunnel walls must be altered.

Work is now being done on the effect of Mach number on separation and eddy-making resistance, as well as on skin-friction. The latter may be purely a temperature effect, the conduction of the heat produced by the shock into the boundary layer raising its kinematic viscosity.

In the usual boundary layer theory, one assumes that the flow outside influences its development and growth, but that there is no reaction by the layer on the main stream, unless or until separation from the surface occurs. Flow near sonic speeds is, on the contrary, extremely sensitive to changes in cross-section, for example in a nozzle, which seems to indicate that change in the thickness of the boundary layer *can* influence the main flow.

Shock waves cannot penetrate to the wall through the layer owing to the comparatively low velocity that must subsist therein, but to the extent that such waves do penetrate they must set up a steep pressure gradient

---

* *Proc. Int. Congress. App. Mech.,* Paris (1946).

in the outer part of the layer. This may cause separation and, as already remarked, certainly reacts on the shock wave in the main flow. In laminar boundary layers the wave is reflected at the limit of penetration as though at a free surface, instead of at the fixed surface of the wall. Just like sound waves reflected at the ends of pipes, a compression is reflected as an expansion at a free surface instead of as a compression, as happens at a fixed surface and would be the case if the shock wave reached the wall. (Such reflections are visible at the confines of a free jet, cf Fig. 51.) The reflected expansions appear in shadow photographs of the shock waves as a fan-shaped system radiating from the reflection level. When the boundary layer is already turbulent where the incident wave meets it an intense compression shock is observed, the shock being approximately normal to the wall.

Fage and Sargent* have found a critical angle of incidence for the wave in this phenomenon, below which regular reflection does not ensue. At an incidence greater than the critical angle, the regular reflection occurs, as stated, at a level out from the wall, while a third wave extends from this point of bifurcation and the wall itself. The two fields of flow which extend downstream from these two wave-fronts have different velocities and are separated by vortex sheets. It is in this respect that supersonic flow along the surface of a solid body with its boundary layer becomes more complex than that in the free jet pictured in Fig. 51, Plate I.

It is a consequence of the equation (51) that along the wave envelope $x \pm \alpha y =$ constant an additional velocity is directed normally to these lines and remains constant alongside each one so that all the stream lines are parallel to each other in the first approximation. The pressure δp to the same approximation is given by $\rho U u$ (where ρ is the undisturbed density) and is thus proportional to u. The resultant of u and v is normal to the wave envelope and of $U - u$ and v is tangential to the surface of the body, so that if U makes an angle ϵ with the surface

$$(U - u) \tan \epsilon = -u \cot \beta$$

Approximately $u = -U\epsilon \tan \beta$ and

$$\delta p = \frac{\rho U^2 \epsilon}{\sqrt{(U^2/a^2 - 1)}} = \rho U^2 \epsilon / \alpha \quad . \quad . \quad . \quad . \quad (53)$$

This gives the pressure coefficient $2\epsilon/\alpha$ at a point on the surface in terms of the local angle of attack ϵ. In two-dimensional flow, pressure effects and the transfer of momentum are only appreciable in two strips, bounded by parallel planes whose inclinations to the direction of flow are equal to β. Compressions and rarefactions are propagated with undiminished intensity along the Mach lines, if the present assumptions are valid, and the formula (53) may be deduced by calculating the action and reaction of the fluid passing through any surface. The total drag of a cylindrical body can

* *Proc. Roy. Soc.*, **A190**, 1 (1947).

then be calculated by integration. It will be noted that the solution fails for $M=1$, while for supersonic speeds it makes the drag coefficient fall if at the same time ϵ does not change much, which is the case for slender pointed cylinders but not for bluff obstacles. Fig. 46 shows the drag coefficient for various shapes and its variation with Mach number.

The increase of pressure, p, at the stagnation point over the stream value p_0 may be predicted, for along the stream tube which strikes it, combining (47) and (49)

$$p=p_0+\frac{1}{2}\rho_0 U^2\left[1+\frac{M^2}{4}+\frac{2-\gamma}{24}M^4 \cdots\right]$$

provided $[(\gamma-1)/2]M^2<1$. This makes p increase rapidly as M increases (cf. Fig. 47).

Supersonic Jets

The other aspect of supersonic flow to which both theoretical and

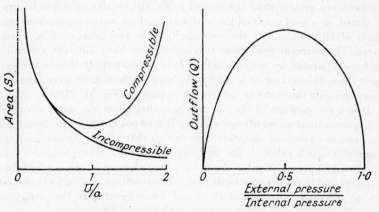

Fig. 48. Variation of area of jet with Mach number.

Fig. 49. Variation of outflow from reservoir with pressure excess.

practical attention has been given is concerned with the flow through nozzles and tubes and into the atmosphere from a reservoir under pressure. As long as compressibility has no part in the process, the outflow from a nozzle will depend solely on its area and the pressure difference between the two sides of it. Moreover, the velocity in an expanding or contracting tube will be inversely as the mean velocity through the section at any place. But if the density of the medium is a function of the pressure and both these diminish as U increases, the cross-section of the jet (S) must ultimately rise as U increases in the supersonic range. Thus, if Q is the outflow per second

$$S=\frac{Q}{\rho U}; \quad \frac{dS}{dU}=-\frac{Q}{\rho U^2}-\frac{Q}{\rho^2 U}\frac{d\rho}{dU} \quad \cdots \quad \cdots \quad (54)$$

putting $dU=-dp/\rho U$ (Bernoulli) and $dp/d\rho=a^2$, where a is the velocity of sound in the gas. dS/dU is negative when $U<a$, reaches a minimum at $U=a$, and is positive when $U>a$ (Fig. 48).

If the process is adiabatic, then as the ratio of the pressure inside to that on the outside increases, the outflow first rises, then reaches a maximum, when the efflux velocity reaches the local velocity of sound, and falls again to zero when the internal pressure is infinite. In a diatomic gas the critical pressure ratio for maximum outflow occurs when the internal is about double the external pressure (Fig. 49).

To get the "cleanest" flow through a nozzle the speed should be brought by contraction of the section up to the speed of sound at a throat, after which the section should gradually widen out to let the pressure down gently from the critical to the atmospheric value without the flow either

leaving the walls or trying to force them outwards, otherwise energy is used up in producing shock waves. Such a tube is called, after the inventor, a Laval nozzle. Fig. 50 shows the section of a Laval nozzle with the variation of Q with distance down the throat (x). If the pressure within the jet where it debouches into the atmosphere is not equal to that in the open air it becomes criss-crossed with stationary shock waves in which the impulse loss is expended (see Fig. 51, Plate I, where a supersonic jet has been silhouetted as it was let directly without expansion of its section into the atmosphere).

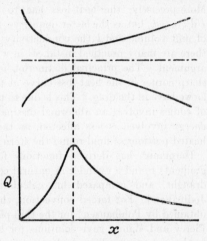

Fig. 50.   Laval nozzle and pressure variation therein.

It will be noted that the two conditions of equality of speed to that of sound in the throat and of internal jet pressure to atmospheric when the jet reaches free space mean that a fresh shape of Laval nozzle is needed for each pressure ratio, also that the final velocity of the jet when "straightened" will, neglecting frictional loss, be given by the upper curve of Fig. 48. Thus, to construct a miniature wind-tunnel, Stanton[*] used a Laval nozzle of the appropriate shape for a given Mach number at the correct pressure ratio and placed model sections in a cylindrical continuation of the expansion tube. To vary Mach number without altering Reynolds number, Ackeret[†] uses a nozzle of plastic material which can be moulded into the correct shape for each change of local sound speed (*vide supra*).

* *Proc. Roy. Soc.*, **A111**, 306 (1926).   † *loc. cit.*

CHAPTER 4

FLUIDS WITH A TEMPERATURE GRADIENT

Temperature Field round a Hot Body

A close analogy exists between the processes by which momentum and heat are transferred from a solid body to the fluid through which it is moving, so that, for example, the drag and the heat-loss expressed in dimensional terms can both be plotted as functions of Reynolds number. More precisely, the heat-loss has to be plotted against the product $Ud/\nu \times c\nu/k$, but as the latter quantity—in which c is the thermal capacity of unit volume and k the conductivity—is a constant for diatomic gases, there are many practical instances in which it may be dismissed from the argument. The principal distinction is to be found in the absence of a sharp corner in the heat-loss curve at the critical Reynolds number such as we have in the drag. This is due to the fact that whereas the formation of eddies involves an abnormal dissipation of motional energy, the heat energy involved is less affected, as the eddies simply swirl the already heated portions of fluid round the stern of the obstacle.

Hermann* has derived functions for the temperature and velocity gradients round a cylinder in natural convection, i.e. in absence of forced draught, and compared his calculations with the measurements of Jodlbauer.† For forced convection, the corresponding solution was first obtained by Pohlhausen‡ for the thin plate parallel to the stream. Later, Piercy and Winny gave solutions for both plate and cylinder, to which further reference will be made.

In each case the temperature function is plotted as the ratio of the value θ at a perpendicular distance to that θ_0 at the surface against a non-dimensional distance, and the curves take the same form for natural and forced convection (provided the plate has its flat surface vertical and the cylinder its axis horizontal). This is to be expected since natural convection may be regarded as a limiting case of forced convection at low fluid velocities, entailed by differences in density of the fluid adjacent to the hot body. In natural convection, however, the dimensionless distance is expressed in terms of Grashof's number, $G=d^3g\beta\theta/\nu^2$, where g is the acceleration of gravity and β the coefficient of expansion of the fluid. In forced convection, on the other hand, the distance parameter is a function of Péclet's number, $P=Udc/k$, where c is the thermal capacity per unit volume and k the thermal conductivity of the fluid.

---

* *V.D.I. Forschungsh.*, **379** (1936). † *Ibid.*, **4**, 157 (1933).
‡ *Zeits. f. ange. Math. u. Mech.*, **1**, 115 (1921).

The solution given by Piercy and Winny* for the cylinder is

$$\frac{\theta}{\theta_0} = \frac{2}{\sqrt{\pi}} \int_0^\infty e^{-x^2} dx \quad \cdots \quad \cdots \quad (55)$$

where x is written for $(2r-d)/d . \sin \xi/2 . \sqrt{P}$, $(r-d)/2$ being the distance from the surface of a point where the temperature excess is θ and ξ the polar co-ordinate of the point reckoned from the front stagnation point. When x is large the equation (55) may be written:

$$\frac{\theta}{\theta_0} = \frac{e^{-x^2}}{x\sqrt{\pi}}$$

On Fig. 52 are given the data for $\xi = \pi/2$, i.e. on a horizontal plane through

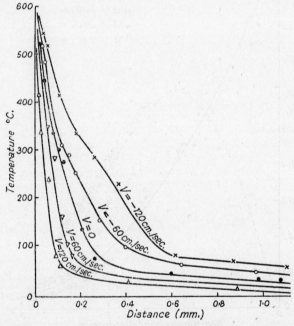

Fig. 52. Temperature gradients in front of cylinder in a stream.

the axis of a hot cylinder ($d=1.3$ cm.) for various upward and downward draughts. On Fig. 53 are shown, by continuous line, data from equation (55), while the broken line is the velocity distribution (after Hermann). The latter curve, as drawn, represents the velocity distribution in natural convection; in forced convection the velocity would rise to the general stream velocity at infinite distance. The boundary layer of velocity, as indicated by the rising gradient, extends to a depth at which the temperature has fallen to roughly half the surface value.

* Phil. Mag., **16**, 390 (1933).

In comparing an experimental distribution—points on Fig. 53, from the author's* measurements—with theory, one is faced with the difficulty that G or P is not a constant through the boundary layer, nor is the temperature at $x=0$ in the fluid necessarily that of the solid. It is usual to select the Péclet number corresponding to the mean temperature at each point in the field and to extrapolate the temperature readings to find θ_0 at $x=0$ and to call this the body temperature. Bearing in mind these approximations, the agreement between the experimental points

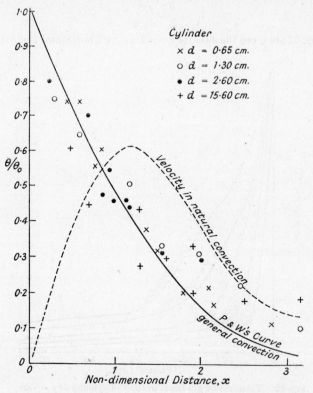

Fig. 53. Temperature and velocity boundary layers of a cylinder.

and theory is fair up to moderate values of x. At larger values of x the temperature measured by thermocouples does not fall as rapidly as theory would have it. This may be due to radiation from the cylinder to the thermometer. This effect will be—in proportion to the convection—greater at greater distances and therefore a larger "correction."

At least up to $x=2$, the general shape of the curve is followed by all experimental results, and at this value of x a common value of 0.2 for

* *Phil. Mag.*, **23**, 681 (1937).

θ/θ_0 is reached. If we define the thickness of the boundary layer δ to conform to this value of the distance parameter, we get the values in the table below. Change in the régime of flow should then be expected at a critical value of d/δ for a given surface temperature. From the experimental results of the author we find a mean critical δ/d of 0·125 as the following table shows:

d	θ_0	CRITICAL		
		U	δ	δ/d
6.5 mm.	450° C.	70 cm. per sec.	0·93 mm.	0·14
,,	580° C.	90 ,, ,, ,,	0·97 ,,	0·15
13 mm.	450° C.	40 cm. per sec.	1·7 mm.	0·13
,,	650° C.	55 ,, ,, ,,	1·85 ,,	0·14
26 mm.	650° C.	40 cm. per sec.	3·1 mm.	0·12

Piercy and Winny's solutions for the relative heat-loss along the contour of the cylinder and the thin plate parallel to the stream are given in Fig. 54. Just as Blasius worked out the velocity distribution in flow along a flat plate with an augmenting boundary layer (cf. p. 30), so Pohlhausen* derived the corresponding temperature distribution.

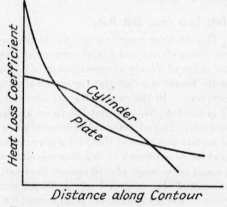

Fig. 54.   Heat flow along contour of flat plate and circular cylinder.

The equation to be solved, neglecting friction, is

$$U\frac{\partial \theta}{\partial x} + V\frac{\partial \theta}{\partial y} = \frac{k}{c}\frac{\partial^2 \theta}{\partial y^2}$$

with the boundary conditions:
$\theta = \theta_0$ at $y = 0$; $\theta = 0$ at $y = \infty$
The equation can be satisfied where θ is a function of $\sqrt{(U\nu/x)}.y$ only and, for a specified value of $c\nu/k$, gives a unique distribution of temperature in terms of this parameter.

Instability of Fluid Heated from Below

When a fluid layer has a gradient of density decreasing as one goes vertically upwards it is stable, but if the gradient is directed contrariwise the heavier fluid tends to take the place of the lighter. Rayleigh† showed

* Z. f. ange. Math. u. Mech., **1**, 115 (1921).   † Phil. Mag., **32**, 529 (1916).

that the criterion in the case of a stratum of height h with extreme difference of density $\delta\rho$ is

$$\frac{\delta\rho}{\rho} < \frac{27\pi^4\nu}{4gh^3}$$

for stability. When the gradient is engendered by a temperature difference $\delta\theta$, Jeffreys* finds

$$\frac{\delta\theta}{\theta} < 1\cdot7\times10^3\frac{\nu}{gh^3}$$

In fact, Chandra† found, using layers of liquid up to 1 cm. deep, that Jeffreys' criterion held only down to $h=6$ mm. Thinner strata had a nearly constant $\delta\theta/\theta\nu k$ of order unity. Two different types of instability characterise the two regions. The deeper layers resolve into rows of little cells of polygonal shape—the "cellular vortices" of Bénard, cf. p. 59 and Fig. 43—whereas the shallower layers tend to break up into strips of continuously ascending material from top to bottom and back of the full depth.

Another type of instability accompanying differences in density occurs when one layer streams over the other or when a jet passes into stationary fluid (cf. Chap. 5).

Heat Loss from Hot Body

This problem may first be treated dimensionally, again separating the two cases of free and forced convection. Some "form factor" involving the shape of a body of revolution or of a cylinder transverse to the stream or the height of a thin plate or length of a pipe parallel to the stream must intervene. In the case of the cylinder the parameter is $Hd/k\theta_0$, wherein H is the heat-loss per unit length and k the thermal conductivity of the medium. Davis‡ collected results in gases and added some of his own in liquids and showed that, for a given shape and disposition of solid, all heat-losses expressed in this dimensionless parameter could be reduced to a single curve when plotted against the Grashof number for free convection or against the reciprocal of the Péclet number (equivalent in diatomic gases to Reynolds number, as aforesaid) for forced convection.

Potential Convection of Cylinder

Boussinesq§ and King‖ have tackled this problem, which is of considerable importance in relation to hot-wire anemometry. Considering an incompressible fluid in two dimensions, the temperature equation is:

$$U\frac{\partial\theta}{\partial x}+V\frac{\partial\theta}{\partial y}=\kappa\left(\frac{\partial^2\theta}{\partial x^2}+\frac{\partial^2\theta}{\partial y^2}\right) \quad . \quad . \quad . \quad . \quad (56a)$$

Here κ is the thermal diffusivity, i.e. the conductivity divided by the

* Proc. Roy. Soc., A118, 195 (1928).   † Proc. Roy. Soc., A164, 231 (1938).
‡ Phil. Mag., 40, 692 (1920); 41, 899 (1921). § Comptes Rendus, 133, 257 (1901).
‖ Phil. Trans., A214, 373 (1914).

thermal capacity per unit volume of fluid, k/c. This equation can be expressed in terms of a velocity potential ϕ and stream function ψ, as:

$$\frac{\partial \theta}{\partial \phi} = \kappa \left(\frac{\partial^2 \theta}{\partial \phi^2} + \frac{\partial^2 \theta}{\partial \psi^2} \right) \quad \cdots \cdots \quad (57)$$

If we assume with Boussinesq that the equipotential lines are also isothermals, the second term only on the right remains, leading to solutions of the type:

$$\theta = \phi^{-1/2} e^{-\frac{\psi^2}{4\kappa\phi}} \quad \cdots \cdots \cdots \quad (58)$$

otherwise more complex solutions involving Bessel functions crop up.

In practice such a thermal potential flow is modified by a temperature boundary layer, in the same way that a velocity potential flow, without the temperature gradient, is modified. In this temperature boundary layer the Péclet number replaces the Reynolds number. When, as in the most important practical applications, these coincide, the two layers have the same thickness—though this does not mean the same thickness as when the body is cold, since the mean viscosity in the layer will depend on its temperature—and the heat is transported by the same mechanism as is momentum. The field of temperature defect is then the same as the field of velocity round the solid. Furthermore, the diffusion of heat into the fluid from the cylinder may be used to study the diffusion of momentum, in turbulence problems (cf. p. 49) or either may be modelled as an actual experiment in diffusion, e.g. of smoke or a dye from the surface of the obstacle into the stream.

Boussinesq[*] eventually derived the following formula for the heat-loss per unit temperature excess:

$$\frac{H}{\theta} = 8 \sqrt{\left(ckU\frac{a}{\pi} \right)}$$

King's[†] formula is similar but with an additional constant. The parabolic relationship between H and U does in fact break down at low velocities, moreover the parabola does not pass through the point $H=0$, $U=0$; King's additive term takes care of this. For low velocities when the natural convection current of the wire becomes important he has another form of equation. King's two formulae are:

$$H = \frac{2\pi k \theta}{\log_e (b/a)} \quad \text{(low speed)} \quad \cdots \quad (59)$$

$$H = [k + 2\sqrt{(\pi k c U a)}] \cdot \theta \quad \text{(high speed)} \quad \cdots \quad (60)$$

in which $b = k e^{1-\gamma}/cU$. The change-over velocity depends on the orientation of the wire, being lower for a horizontal than for a vertical cylinder. Thomas[‡] quotes the following values for the mean natural convection

---

[*] *Comptes Rendus*, **133**, 257 (1901).   [†] *Phil. Trans. Roy. Soc.*, **A214**, 373 (1914).
[‡] *Proc. Phys. Soc.*, **32**, 291 (1920).

current U_0 from a wire 0·0784 mm. diameter extending horizontally across a vertical tube 2 cm. wide.

θ_0	135	191	245	315	420	535	677° C.
U_0	3·1	4·0	5·4	7·0	9·1	12·2	15·9 cm. per sec.

The "Dust-free Space"

The dust-free space surrounding a heated cylinder in a dusty or misty atmosphere, discovered by Tyndall,[*] has recently been quantitatively examined by Miyake[†] and by Watson[‡]. Whatever the ultimate origin of the phenomenon—and rival theories will be found in the papers just cited—it is obvious from the published photographs that the configuration of the dust-free space conforms to the temperature (or velocity) boundary layer. That being so, it may be of interest to compare measurements of the boundary layer with those of the dust-free space. As the measurements made by Miyake and Watson concern natural convection we will select the results of Jodlbauer–Hermann for the comparison.

The dimensionless boundary layer thickness δ/d in natural convection is inversely proportional to $(d^3 g \beta \theta_0/\nu^2)^{1/4}$, i.e. $\delta \propto d^{1/4} \theta_0^{-1/4} \nu^{1/2}$. The exact value of the exponent n in the assumed proportionality, $\nu \propto \theta^n$, will depend on the range of temperature concerned, but taking $n=1$ as an attempt to cover a moderate range, we shall get $\delta \propto d^{1/4} \theta_0^{1/4}$. Now Watson used two rods 4·6 and 9 mm. diameter respectively, together with a wire 0·001 in. diameter. The measured values of δ (dust-free layer) agree moderately well with the relation $\delta \propto d^{1/4}$. For instance, the thinner rod and wire (ratio of diameters 18 : 1) have dust-free spaces of relative thickness 1·9 : 1 at 220° C. The agreement is not so good in the temperature variation; instead of an exponent $\frac{1}{4}$, Watson would put $\frac{1}{2}$, while Miyake prefers 0·7. Apart from discrepancy between the experimental results of the two observers the disagreement with theory may be in part imputed to our assumption of a constant ν throughout the boundary layer.

Evaporation from a Liquid Surface

The problem of evaporation from a liquid surface into an air stream is likewise closely related to the subjects under discussion. In place of the Péclet number, or its reciprocal, the parameter Ud/D, where D is the vapour diffusivity, must be introduced. Pasquill[§] has carried out experiments of this nature, exposing filter-papers soaked in liquid in a wind-tunnel so that the air glided over their surface, and measuring the loss of weight in a known time. At a given wind speed the rate of evaporation E per unit difference of vapour pressure (saturation p_1—atmospheric p_0) multiplied

* *Proc. Roy. Inst.*, **6**, 3 (1870).　　　† *Rep. Aero. Inst. Tokyo*, **10**, 85 (1935).
‡ *Trans. Farad. Soc.*, **32**, 1073 (1936).　　§ *Proc. Roy. Soc.*, **A182**, 75 (1943).

by the absolute temperature Θ and divided by the molecular weight M was found to be proportional to a power of D, thus:

$$\frac{E\Theta}{M(p_1-p_0)} \propto D^n$$

Pasquill's experiments, which were performed with a number of organic liquids, of which the chief was bromobenzene, and water, gave $n=\frac{1}{4}$, approximately, as appropriate to the "one-seventh power law" (cf. p. 47) of velocity distribution over the plate. Presumably n will vary with the velocity profile. Heat transfer measurements from hot plates are in agreement with the same power law and value of n. The exponent of U in heat transfer to a turbulent stream is 0·8.

Hot-wire Anemometer

If a wire be heated by a constant electric current i and its electric resistance R allowed to vary in a measured manner in a steady wind, we may write $H=i^2R/J$ calories ($J=$mechanical equivalent of heat), while the resistance is related to the temperature in accordance with the formula $R=R_0(1+\alpha\theta)$. ($R=$hot resistance, $R_0=$cold resistance, $\alpha=$a coefficient for the material.) Combining these with (60) to cover the more generally likely case, we have

$$\frac{RR_0}{R-R_0}=l_1k+m_1\sqrt{(kcU)}$$

l_1 and m_1 are constants for a particular wire, while the other factors relate to the circumambient fluid.

The hot-wire anemometer usually takes the form of a short length of platinum or nickel wire about 1/1000 in. in diameter supported on a fork and heated by a current of about 1/10 ampere. It is more commonly employed in gases, but may also be used in liquids. The greater density and specific heat of the latter makes the instrument less sensitive for a given temperature excess. The electrical resistance is usually measured on a sensitive Wheatstone bridge or potentiometer.

Fig. 55 shows calibration curves for a wire in various fluids, the velocity being plotted quadratically. The value of $\sqrt{(kc)}$ for the four media are respectively: water 0·039, syrup 0·025, paraffin 0·0128, air 0·00011. The calibration was effected by whirling the wire on an arm through the medium in a circle of which the length of the wire formed part of the radius.

When using the hot wire in close proximity to a solid wall or model in a wind-tunnel, a correction to its reading is necessary by virtue of the fact that heat is conducted to the boundary as well as carried away by convection. This is more important at small fluid velocities. In fact, when the fluid is still, the wire indicates an apparent velocity in virtue of this conducted heat. When the wire is near a plane conductor, this cooling is readily calculated by the method of images following an established method of calculation of the electrical capacitance of a cylinder near a plate, but the theory becomes difficult when the boundary layer of the plate is in motion, embracing as it does both the thermodynamics and the hydrodynamics of a fluid of small viscosity, but Piercy and the author* have established the correction *in air* by whirling a vertical platinum wire at known speeds round a circle of slightly larger radius than a fixed metal cylinder and measuring the loss of heat. Results are shown in Fig. 56, from which it is apparent that the heat loss by conduction and consequently any correction to the apparent velocities indicated by the hot wire in a stream become negligible beyond a limiting distance (indicated by the chain line) from the plate. This limit comes closer to the wall as the local speed in which the wire finds itself goes up, because the conduction draught is blown further downstream before it strikes the

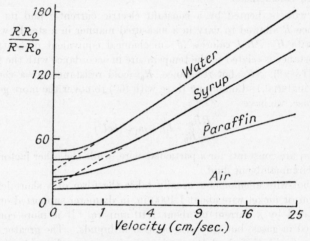

Fig. 55.   Calibration curves of hot-wire anemometer.

cylinder and the heat-loss *by conduction* depends inversely on the path length that the heat has to flow between the hot and the cold solid. It should be noted that Zijnen's results for the flow along a flat plate (p. 31) were all over-corrected, as he only determined the curve for $U = 0$ and used this to correct all his readings at each and every speed.

Hot-wire Anemometry in Unsteady Flow

When a heated cylinder is subjected to S.H.M. at all but very low frequencies, the "thermal inertia" prevents it following the change of velocity relative to the fluid with exactitude. If its electrical resistance is measured on an instrument capable of following the fluctuations such as the cathode-ray oscillograph it is found that the resistance of the wire

* *A.R.C.O., R. and M.*, No. 1224 (1928).

consists effectively of two parts, i.e. a steady drop plus an alternating variation of twice the frequency of the motion but of smaller amplitude. (The octave of the frequency of oscillation arises because the wire is unable to distinguish between motion to left and right, so that its resistance falls twice in each period of the S.H.M.)

Writing (60) in the simpler form, for steady conditions,

$$i^2R=(l_1+m_1\sqrt{U})\theta \qquad . \qquad . \qquad . \qquad . \qquad . \qquad . \qquad (61)$$

During the attainment of equilibrium there is another term in $d\theta/d$

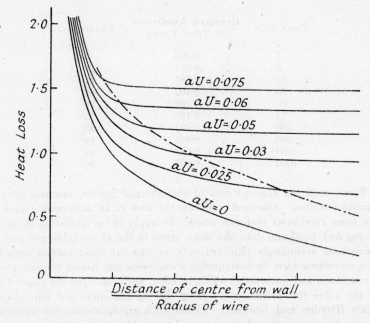

Fig. 56. Correction to hot-wire anemometer for proximity of wall.

which intervenes. Making the same substitution of electrical resistance for temperature, we have

$$\frac{f}{R_0a}=i^2R-(l_1+m_1\sqrt{U})\frac{R-R_0}{R_0a} \qquad . \qquad . \qquad . \qquad (62)$$

where f=thermal capacity of wire in joules per degree. Setting R_1=final resistance, we can combine (61) and (62) to get

$$\frac{f}{R_0a}=\frac{i^2R_0(R_1-R)}{R_1-R_0}$$

that is,

$$\frac{dR}{dt}=\frac{1}{\lambda}(R_1-R)$$

where λ is a temporal factor which represents the thermal inertia of the hot wire.

$$\lambda = \frac{f(R_1 - R_0)}{ai^2 R_0{}^2} \qquad \ldots \ldots \quad (63)$$

The amplitude of the velocity indication of the anemometer is reduced from the true (very low frequency value) in the reciprocal ratio of $\sqrt{(1 + \lambda^2 \omega^2)}$ in a draught of frequency $\omega/2\pi$. The phase of its response is also delayed by the angle $\tan^{-1}(\lambda\omega)$. The table which follows shows (after Dryden and Kuethe*) these two factors.

Frequency	Relative Amplitude to True Value	Phase Lag
1	0·995	6°
5	0·884	28°
10	0·687	47°
20	0·402	60°
50	0·186	79°
75	0·125	83°
100	0·094	85°
200	0·043	89°
500	0·018	90°
1000	0·008	90°

Faced with the consequences of this thermal inertia, one can adopt various remedies. One could calibrate the wire as an anemometer under the same conditions that one intends to apply it by oscillating it on a tuning-fork to obtain data like those given in the above table and make corrections accordingly (Richardson†), or one can disembarrass oneself of a correcting term by introducing a compensating circuit consisting of a resistance and inductance which in effect adds on a further phase lag to the value just calculated to bring the lag full circle and into phase again (Dryden and Kuethe‡). Under such circumstances the thermal inertia disappears, though it may not be possible to effect the compensation for all frequencies.

Amplifiers may be introduced into anemometer circuits which will transform the shape of the calibration curve, such as the parabola which is usually obtained between resistance and velocity (cf. equation (60)), into any shape desired, in particular into a straight line. This may be done by feeding the potential difference across the hot wire into the grid of a variable-mu valve—first done by Luneau§— as shown in Fig. 57.

A further stage may then be added in which the electrical impedance of a resistance and inductance in the anode circuit necessary to compensate for the frequency characteristic of the wire is introduced. Such a doubly

---

* *N.A.C.A. Rep.*, 320 (1929).   † *Proc. Roy. Soc.*, **A112**, 522 (1926).
‡ *loc. cit.*   § *Aeronautique*, **15**, 232 (1933).

compensated anemometer should give a response proportional to the amplitude of a velocity fluctuation (for instance in turbulent flow) independently of the frequency of the latter, but at the loss of a certain sensitivity (Fig. 58). The way in which the electrical filter evens out the frequency response is illustrated in Fig. 59 (after Wattendorf and Kuethe*).

The hot-wire, even when compensated for frequency, still requires correction on the lines indicated on Fig. 56 when used to measure fluctuating flow in the boundary layer of a solid wall or obstacle. For instance, this has been done in constructing the velocity-amplitude curves of Fig. 28.

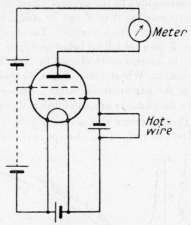

Fig. 57.   Hot-wire anemometer with linear response.

Measurement of Correlation Coefficients

If two hot wires are placed at two points in a stream, either along the x or the y or the z axis, and the fluctuating potentials across them applied to the two pairs of plates of a cathode-ray oscillograph, the horizontal and vertical deflections of the electron beam can represent the magnitude and relative phase of the simultaneous velocity fluctuations at the two locations. When the correlation coefficient $R=1$, so that the two oscillations are in phase, the electron spot traces a straight line on the screen. Changes in relative amplitude and phase corresponding to R less

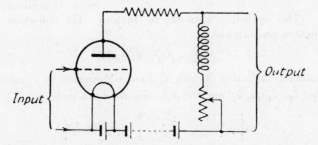

Fig. 58.   Circuit for frequency correction of hot-wire anemometer.

than 1 will cause the spot to trace out an ellipse whose minor and major axes are in the ratio $\sqrt{[(1-R)/(1+R)]}$, so that complete incoherence results in a circle. Prandtl and Reichardt† devised and tested this method and

* *Physics*, **5**, 133 (1934).   † *Naturwissenschaften*, **26**, 404 (1938).

it was subsequently used to study correlations in the flow behind grids in a wind-tunnel. In the latter case, where the fluctuations of turbulence are not S.H.M., the ellipse does not remain still, as it would in periodic flow, but a photograph taken with a time exposure gives a picture which corresponds to the average phase and relative amplitude over the time of exposure, so that R can be still inferred from the rather hazy outline of the figure which results. The method is only suitable when the value of R does not fall far below unity, i.e. for locations of the wires not far apart.

In another method used by G. I. Taylor,* the two wires are arranged in separate Wheatstone bridges, so that in steady motion there is no current in the galvanometer arms. Out-of-balance currents in these arms due to fluctuations are amplified and compensated for frequency (*vide supra*). These currents give severally $\sqrt{(\overline{u_1^2})}$ and $\sqrt{(\overline{u_2^2})}$, but when they are fed to the two coils of an electrodynamometer a deflection of one coil relative to the other results of value proportional to the products of the current in the coils, i.e. to $\overline{u_1 u_2}$. Hence R is calculated (cf. p. 53).

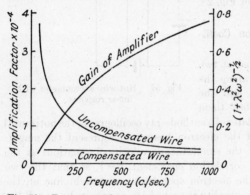

Fig. 59.   Response of frequency-corrected hot-wire.

Alternatively, a fraction ζ_1 of the first galvanometer branch current may be tapped off on a potentiometer, and ζ_2 from the second, led to the same amplifier and the mean square of the output read on a thermo-milliammeter. (This method is also due to Taylor.) The deflection of the instrument is proportional to

$$\zeta_1^2 \overline{u_1}^2 + \zeta_2^2 \overline{u_2}^2 - 2\zeta_1 \zeta_2 \overline{u_1 u_2}$$

The minimum deflection δ_1 with ζ_2 fixed corresponds to a value of ζ_1 such that $\zeta_2 = \zeta_1 \overline{u_1 u_2}/\overline{u_2}^2$ and the deflection itself is a measure of

$$\zeta_1 \left[\overline{u_1}^2 + \frac{\overline{u_1 u_2}}{\overline{u_2}^2} - \frac{2\overline{u_1 u_2}^2}{\overline{u_2}^2} \right] = \zeta_1 \overline{u_1}^2 (1 - R^2)$$

If ζ_2 is now made zero, one can get a deflection δ_2 proportional to $\zeta_1 \overline{u_1}^2$. Finally,

$$\frac{\delta_1}{\delta_2} = 1 - R^2$$

* *Proc. Roy. Soc.*, **A157**, 537 (1936).

Convection at Supersonic Speeds

Santon* has carried out measurements of the heat supply necessary to maintain a platinum or nickel wire at dull-red heat when placed in a miniature supersonic wind-tunnel of the Laval nozzle type (Fig. 50). In accordance with (60) the heat dissipated from the wire is roughly proportional to $\sqrt{U}$ at subsonic speeds, although the coefficient connecting the two varies somewhat in conformity with the change in drag, such as we have already remarked in forced convection (p. 72). On this point compare the subsonic portion of the curve shown in Fig. 60 with the variation in the opposite sense of drag with Mach number for the cylinder (Fig. 46). This former curve of heat dissipation H against $\sqrt{(\rho U/\rho_0)}$,

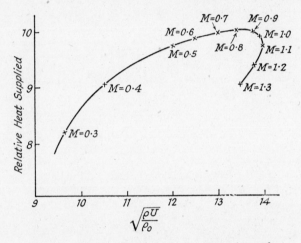

Fig. 60. Heat-loss from hot wire at supersonic speeds.

after rising until a Mach number of 0·8 is reached, falls thereafter at supersonic speeds. Whereas the rise is probably to be correlated with the increase of drag, the succeeding fall is probably due to heat derived from the friction and shock wave production, so that a smaller debit has to be made up from the electric battery. An extension of this work to higher Mach numbers is desirable, but difficult on account of the liability to breakage of the wires. Weske,† who has repeated these results, found tungsten the best metal to use.

The heat of friction referred to above is dependent on the quantity $\frac{1}{2}(\gamma-1).M^2$, which we have met in the relations (49) of the preceding chapter. This, expressed in ratio to the fractional excess of temperature of the body over the fluid—$\delta\theta/\theta$, where $\delta\theta$ is the temperature excess—is sometimes called the Joule–Kelvin parameter. The heat of friction

* Comptes Rendus, **196**, 625 (1933).   † N.A.C.A., Tech. Note No. 880 (1943).

produces in the boundary layer a further reduction in ν, over and above that due to the heat transferred from the solid (p. 68). Von Kármán sets out the following empirical formula for the drag coefficient due to skin-friction in the laminar layer:

$$\frac{1}{c_D} = A\sqrt{(Re)}\left\{1+\frac{\gamma-1}{2}M^2\right\}^{\frac{1}{4}}$$

A being a constant varying with M of value 4/5 approximately.

CHAPTER 5

LIQUID HAVING A FREE SURFACE

If a liquid presents an interface between two phases in the form either of a free surface with air or its own vapour or of an interface with another liquid of less density, phenomena can occur at the surface which are associated with an extension or contraction of its area or with a rising or falling of parts of it. Such changes in superficial area involve the "surface tension," measured as the force per unit length in the surface σ and the acceleration of gravity g.

Waves on a Free Surface

First we shall ignore the effect of surface tension and viscosity and think of the waves which can be set up in the free surface between a liquid

Fig. 61.   Stream-lines of surface waves on deep water.

and a gas by the relative motion of the two phases such as occurs on a stretch of water under the action of the wind.

It is a matter for observation that in the simplest form of wave that may be set up, the individual particles in the surface trace out circles (cf. Fig. 61, which also shows the stream lines). From the point of view of an observer travelling with the waves at velocity c, the flow is steady and Bernoulli's theorem can be applied to it. If a particle describes a circle of radius r with frequency n its velocity round the circle is $2\pi rn$, so that to the observer its horizontal speed in a crest is $U_1=c-2\pi rn$ and $U_2=c+2\pi rn$ in a trough. As the surface remains at atmospheric pressure, Bernoulli gives $U_2{}^2-U_1{}^2=2gh=4gr$, whence

$$c=\frac{g}{2\pi n}=\sqrt{\frac{g\lambda}{2\pi}} \qquad . \quad . \quad . \quad . \quad (64)$$

since the wavelength

$$\lambda=\frac{c}{n}. \qquad . \quad . \quad . \quad . \quad . \quad (65)$$

The wave velocity thus varies with the wavelength, unlike ordinary sound waves, and if there are mixed wavelengths present "dispersion"

87

ensues. Although such waves will interfere at any instant there will be a series of equispaced peaks, or maxima, among the crests, whose rate of movement, though uniform, is not the same as that of any individual set of waves in the group. This rate of movement is known as the "group velocity."

Thus, if there are two superposed sets of waves of frequency n and n' with wavelengths λ and λ' respectively, their resultant is

$$A\left\{\sin 2\pi\left(nt-\frac{x}{\lambda}\right)+\sin 2\pi\left(n't-\frac{x}{\lambda'}\right)\right\}$$

$$=2A\sin\pi(\overline{n+n'}t-\overline{\lambda+\lambda'}x)\cos\pi(\overline{n-n'}t+\overline{\lambda-\lambda'}x)$$

At any instant t_1 the peaks are to be found at x_1 such that the cosine is 1, i.e. where

$$(n-n')t_1=(\lambda-\lambda')x_1$$

The velocity with which these thread the system, the group velocity,

$$c=\frac{x_1}{t_1}=\frac{n-n'}{\lambda-\lambda'} \quad . \quad . \quad . \quad . \quad . \quad . \quad . \quad . \quad . \quad (66)$$

In a manifold system of many frequencies distributed about a mean n_0,

$$c=\frac{\partial n_0}{\partial\lambda}=\frac{1}{2}\sqrt{\frac{g\lambda}{2\pi}}=\frac{1}{2}c \quad . \quad . \quad . \quad . \quad . \quad (67)$$

by (64) and (65).

Such "gravity waves" can also be set up at an interface between two liquids or between strata of the same liquid or gas at different densities, e.g. between fresh and salt water. Such waves often break down into instability and cause turbulent mixing.

Kelvin[*] showed that when two fluids of densities ρ and ρ' are moving one over the other with relative velocity U, waves travel with velocity relative to the mean velocity of the two fluids, given by

$$c^2=\frac{\rho-\rho'}{\rho+\rho'}\cdot\frac{g\lambda}{2\pi}-\frac{\rho\rho'}{(\rho+\rho')^2}U^2$$

Solutions involving the frequency of the surface oscillation are, however, imaginary if

$$\frac{g\lambda}{2\pi}\frac{\rho^2-\rho'^2}{\rho\rho'}<U^2,$$

meaning that the interface is unstable when the wavelength is such as to make the expression on the left less than the square of the relative velocity. In practice these considerations will be modified by viscosity in three main directions:

(1) There will be velocity gradients across the interface, at which the two fluids will have a common velocity;

[*] *Phil. Mag.*, **42**, 374 (1871). The proof is given in Lamb's *Hydrodynamics*, §§ 223, 268.

(2) the shearing forces across the boundary will cause its breakdown and some mixing of the two fluids;

(3) viscosity will damp waves and other disturbances. Surface tension, if any, between the two layers will further inhibit the instability of the surface.

When the relative velocity of the two liquids becomes too great to sustain stable waves, turbulent mixing ensues, the tops of the waves being broken off as at the free surface of the sea. During this régime, the fast-moving liquid pumps the slower one into its domain. This process is very important for the production of emulsions and of cyclones in the atmosphere on a large scale (cf. p. 75). Keubgan* has studied the theory of the mixing of two fluid currents having a relative velocity U with the formation of laminar boundary layers, whose thickness proves to be capable of expression in terms of a Blasius parameter $\sqrt{(2\nu x/U)}$ for each medium. A "mixture parameter" $\rho'/\rho . \sqrt{(\nu'/\nu)}$ is also found to be significant.

Effect of Surface Tension: Ripples

Suppose a section of the free surface to be bent by the passage of the wave into the form shown in Fig. 62. The surface has been stretched from its original shape, where it lay along the axis of x, and as a result forces per unit length σ act as indicated and these

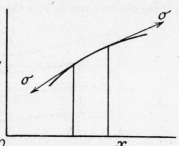

Fig. 62. Forces on element of surface wave.

together with that of gravity tend to restore the *status quo*. Taking $y = A \sin 2\pi . x/\lambda$ to represent the form of the wave, the restoring force due to surface tension on unit length of the wave-front and of unit width (perpendicular to the plane of the paper) is

$$-\sigma\left[\left\{\frac{dy}{dx}+\frac{d}{dx}\left(\frac{dy}{dx}\right).\delta x\right\}-\frac{dy}{dx}\delta x\right]=-\sigma\frac{d^2y}{dx^2}.\delta x=+\frac{4\pi^2}{\lambda^2}\sigma y\delta x$$

replacing the sines of the angles by the slopes of the curve at corresponding points, i.e. supposing displacements and therefore slopes small. Meanwhile the restoring force due to gravity is the weight of the liquid in the section enclosed by the two vertical lines, i.e. $g\rho\delta x$.

Thus the effect of surface tension is an addition to g in (64) of an amount $4\pi^2\sigma/\lambda^2\rho$ and the formula for velocity under both actions is

$$c=\sqrt{\left[\frac{\lambda}{2\pi}\left(g+\frac{4\pi^2\sigma}{\lambda^2 g}\right)\right]} \quad . \quad . \quad . \quad . \quad (68)$$

Examination of this formula shows that σ is only of import when λ is small, that as λ increases the velocity at first falls but afterwards rises,

* *Rep. Nat. Bureau Stand.*, **32**, 303 (1944).

the minimum occurring (as may be verified by differentiation) when $\lambda=\sqrt{(4\pi^2\sigma/g\rho)}$. For water, the critical λ is 1·7 cm. and the corresponding value of c is 23 cm. per sec.

Waves on Liquid of Finite Depth

In this case the particles at the surface execute ellipses (Fig. 63) compounded of a vertical motion, $A \sin 2\pi nt$, and a horizontal motion, $B \cos 2\pi nt$. The wave may be represented as

$$\zeta=A \cos 2\pi\left(nt-\frac{x}{\lambda}\right)$$

where ζ is the elevation at x above normal level. Applying Bernoulli to the surface layer, the bed being at depth h, we get

$$\frac{1}{2}\rho c^2\left(\frac{\zeta}{h+\zeta}\right)^2+g\rho\zeta=\frac{1}{2}\rho c^2$$

for if the observer travels with the wave and U is the horizontal velocity

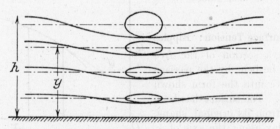

Fig. 63.   Particle motions in waves in shallow liquid.

of surface particles as seen by him, $U(\zeta+h)=c\zeta$. When ζ is small compared to h, we must have

$$c=\sqrt{(gh)} \quad \ldots \quad \ldots \quad \ldots \quad (69)$$

or with surface tension,

$$c=\sqrt{\left\{\left(g+\frac{4\pi^2\sigma}{\lambda^2\rho}\right)h\right\}} \quad \ldots \quad \ldots \quad (70)$$

Particles at the bed can, in the absence of friction, have the same horizontal velocity in their orbit as those standing over them, which is

$$\frac{c}{h}A \cos 2\pi\left(nt-\frac{x}{\lambda}\right)$$

but the vertical displacement and velocity amplitude must fall steadily from the surface value ζ_0 to zero at the bed, so that at a height y above the bed

$$\zeta=\frac{\zeta_0}{h}2\pi nA \sin 2\pi\left(nt-\frac{x}{\lambda}\right)$$

A particle at this elevation executes an ellipse of which the semi-axes, vertical and horizontal, are respectively yA/h and $\lambda A/2\pi h$. In deriving

(69) the vertical motion was neglected, which is justified only if the surface amplitude is small.

In terms of a velocity potential, the equation of motion is

$$\frac{\partial^2 \phi}{\partial t^2} + g\frac{\partial \phi}{\partial y} = 0 \quad \cdots \cdots \cdots \quad (71)$$

for, as the pressure over the surface must be atmospheric, Bernoulli's equation for the surface is $\partial\phi/\partial t = g\zeta$, while the vertical component of particle velocity must equal the velocity of the surface itself there, i.e.

$$\frac{\partial \zeta}{\partial t} = -\left[\frac{\partial \phi}{\partial y}\right]_{y=h}$$

We assume, then, that $\phi = E \cos(2\pi x/\lambda)$ multiplied by a time function (S.H.M.). Substituting in (71) we find that E must be a hyperbolic function of the type $\cosh(2\pi/\lambda)(y+h)$, bearing in mind that $\partial\phi/\partial y$ must be zero at the bed $y = -h$.

By applying Bernoulli in the form

$$\frac{p}{\rho} = \frac{\partial \phi}{\partial t} - gy$$

we can derive the pressure amplitude in the wave system at y as

$$\delta p = g\rho\frac{\cosh 2\pi(y+h)/\lambda}{\cosh 2\pi h/\lambda} = g\rho\left(\cosh 2\pi\frac{y}{\lambda} + \sinh 2\pi\frac{y}{\lambda}\tanh 2\pi\frac{h}{\lambda}\right) \quad (72)$$

when the wave amplitude at the surface is 1. The pressure amplitude therefore decreases to $\rho g \operatorname{sech} 2\pi h/\lambda$ at the bed in place of the static value ρgh to which it tends as the wavelength gets very long.

The quantity in the bracket of equation (72) is plotted for various values of h/λ against y/λ on Fig. 64.

Instruments for delineating wave-height and "swell" employ a measurement of the varying pressure on the sea-bed. Since it is necessary that the instrument when lowered to the bed shall reach equilibrium as to its internal pressure with the mean hydrostatic pressure there, the principle of the equalisation chamber is employed. This consists of a large vessel into which the sea can leak at its base, the upper end being coupled pneumatically by a pipe to the interior of the instrument. The latter may take the form of a capsule of about 1 litre capacity covered with a flexible membrane exposed to the sea. If the connection between the capsule and the equalisation chamber and between the latter and the sea have a high hydraulic resistance, then when a quick change of sea pressure occurs, the membrane will communicate it to the capsule before the main chamber has time to respond and a difference of air pressure will be set up between the capsule and main chamber which can be recorded and related to the rate of change of the pressure in the sea. At the same time slow changes of hydrostatic pressure such as are caused by the tidal ebb and flow will not affect the instrument, as there will be time for equalisation to take place *via* the leak. (A similar principle is employed on aircraft instruments which record "rate of climb" by the rate of change of local atmospheric pressure.)

Fig. 65 is a diagram of the sea-pressure recording instrument devised by the author.* The "capsule" c has a rubber membrane r stretched across a flange above it, and the difference across the leak l between the air pressure inside it and the larger chamber below (which is connected to a separate and still larger "equalisation pot") is recorded by a syphon bellows b such as are used on certain types of microbarograph. Such sensitivity is essential because the pressure differences to be measured normally amount to a few centimetres of water only. As the bellows breathe, a tag on the lower end moves in front of the focus of a beam of light from the pea-lamp on the left and so varies the amount of light falling on the photo-electric cell p on the right, the current from which, recorded on shore, is an indication of the position of the tag. This is related by a previous calibration to the pressure difference. The "leak" or "resistance" consists of 3 cm. of 0·5 mm. inside diameter copper tube.

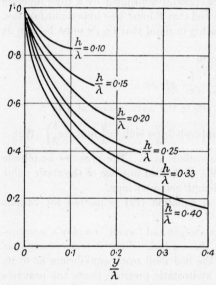

Fig. 64.   Pressure amplitudes beneath waves.

The recorded pressure difference under a system of surface waves of given amplitude is not, even after a correction has been made when necessary for the reduction of pressure that the leak may involve, equal to that amplitude in feet of water, as (72) shows. This would only be true for very long waves like the tides, ignoring for the moment the effect of the leak. Ordinary water waves and "swell" produce a smaller effect than their amplitude would indicate, because of the "interference" produced by neighbouring crests and troughs; in fact at depths of a few fathoms this effect of phase interference, which increases as the wave-length of the surface waves decreases, completely wipes out the pressure amplitudes due to the little waves, but gives a record of the longer motions which characterise swell. The significant quantity is h/λ, as Fig. 64 shows.

Wave-making Drag of Floating Bodies

Everyone will have noticed that the passage of a boat over calm water sets up diverging wave-fronts from prow and stern which are similar in

* *Phil. Mag.*, **37**, 25 (1946).

appearance to a section through a system of shock waves from a projectile
(Fig. 45). Like the latter, these surface waves involve a wave-making
resistance experienced by the boat which overrides the skin-friction along
the hull and, often, the eddy-making dissipation in the wake. Besides
Reynolds number as a criterion, the drag must also be concerned with
some parameter involving g, since the liquid is raised against gravity in
the crests and lowered in the troughs. With the speed and the linear
dimension of the craft as companions we can only construct such a
parameter in the form U^2/gd, which is known as the Froude number (Fr)
of the flow after the pioneer experimenter on the drag of model ships.

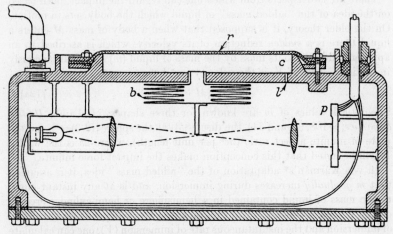

Fig. 65. Wave-pressure recorder.

Over the range of speeds for which the drag is proportional to U^2 and
nearly independent of Re (cf. Fig. 12) we may write

$$F = c_D \cdot \frac{1}{2}\rho U^2 d^2 f\left(\frac{gd}{U^2}\right)$$

If the drag be measured on a model and at full scale at corresponding
speeds to make U^2/d the same for each, we can measure c_D on the model
and transfer it to full scale. It is usually the force that is required to
tow the model along the surface of water in a canal or basin that is
measured. The coefficient for skin-friction alone, per unit area of wetted
surface, was estimated by Froude* from the force needed to tow thin
plates at the same speed edgewise through the water.

Impact on a Liquid Surface

When a solid body strikes a water surface it experiences a diminution
of velocity which may be regarded as a consequence of the conservation of

* *Trans. Inst. Nav. Arch.*, **17** (1877).

momentum, if the body is supposed to pick up and take with it a certain quantity of the liquid known as the "added" or "virtual" mass. For the sphere this added mass is the volume of liquid in the space $\frac{2}{3}\pi a^3$, i.e. half the volume of the sphere. (For proof of this, cf. Lamb, *Hydrodynamics*, §92). Von Kármán* supposed that the same increment could be applied to any solid having axial symmetry, even the sphere itself, if one set the added mass equal to the volume of liquid in a hemisphere based on the wetted perimeter at each instant.

Theoretical Aspects of Impact on Liquids

There are two aspects from which one can regard the impact, both based on the idea of the "added mass" of liquid which the body sets in motion. On the older theory, it is supposed that when a body of mass M enters a liquid there is a *sudden* reduction of its velocity, which is ascribed to an apparent addition to its mass by the mass of liquid (m) set instantaneously in motion. Thus if V_0 is the velocity just before impact, V_1 just after:

$$MV_0 = (M+m)V_1 \qquad \qquad (72a)$$

Theoretical values of m are known for three shapes (cf. Lamb, *Hydrodynamics*, §§108, 92, and 71), the disc [$(8/3)c^3$], the sphere [$(2/3)\pi c^3$], and the plate of infinite aspect ratio (πc^2 per unit length), where $2c$ is the width. It will be noted that this conception makes the impact force infinite.

In von Kármán's* adaptation of the "added mass" idea, it is assumed that m *gradually* increases during immersion, and is at any instant equal to the mass of liquid contained in a hemisphere or hemi-cylinder erected on the wetted perimeter. Knowing how the latter depends on the depth of immersion and the instantaneous rate of immersion (V), one can calculate the force : time curve for the impact in the form of $\partial/\partial t(mV)$ against t.

Calculation of Impact Forces

If an axially symmetrical body hits a liquid at a speed V_0, the force at any subsequent instant

$$F = -M\frac{\partial V}{\partial t} = \frac{\partial}{\partial t}(mV) = \frac{\partial}{\partial t}\left(\frac{2}{3}\pi c^3 \rho V\right) = \frac{2}{3}\pi c^3 \rho \frac{\partial V}{\partial t} + 2\pi c^2 \rho V^2 \frac{\partial c}{\partial h}$$

where h is the depth of immersion and c the radius of the wetted perimeter.

Example 1. Sphere $h = a - \sqrt{(a^2-c^2)}$, $\partial h/\partial c = c/\sqrt{(a^2-c^2)}$;

whence
$$F = -\frac{m}{M}F + 2\pi c\sqrt{(a^2-c^2)}.V\rho^2$$

or (with (72a))
$$\frac{F}{\rho V_0^2} = \frac{2\pi c\sqrt{(a^2-c^2)}}{(1+m/M)^3}$$

The maximum value of this when M is large compared to m occurs when $c = a/\sqrt{2}$ and is then πc^2.

* *N.A.C.A.*, *Tech. Note* No. 32 (1930).

Example 2. Cone of semi-angle γ; $\partial h/\partial c = \cot \gamma$:

$$\frac{F}{\rho V_0{}^2} = \frac{2\pi c^2 . \tan \gamma}{(1 + m/M)^3}$$

The maximum value of this occurs when $m = \frac{1}{2}M$ and is then $0.86 \tan \gamma . c^2$.

It will be noticed that this theory would still make the impact force of a *disc* infinite, since it takes no account of the sideways escape of liquid to form a splash. Wagner* modified the theory in this respect and applied it to obtuse-angled prisms, such as the hull of a seaplane. The theory probably breaks down at the limit of very acute angles, since the "displacement" of liquid by the volume of the immersed segment is then comparable with the added mass of the liquid set in motion.

Kreps† introduced the resistance experienced by the body during

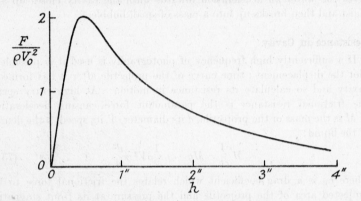

Fig. 66. Force of impact of sphere on water.

immersion. The equation of motion then becomes, neglecting buoyancy, surface tension, and compressibility:

$$M\frac{\partial V}{\partial t} = -\frac{\partial}{\partial t}(mV) + Mg - c_D(\pi c^2)\left(\frac{1}{2}\rho V^2\right)$$

When the velocity of impact is small the last term is unimportant, but the gravity term is not; *per contra* when the velocity is very large. In the latter the case, measured decelerations will deviate more from the theoretical as c_D is greater, i.e. for blunt-nosed projectiles.

Values of the impact force as the body strikes the surface can be derived from cinematograph films of the entry in terms of the instantaneous values of the deceleration. These compare favourably, within the accuracy of the measurement, with von Kármán's theory. Fig. 66 shows $F/\rho V_0{}^2$ plotted against h for a sphere of mass 12,000 gm. dropped on water from 1 meter (Richardson‡).

* Z. f. ange. Math. u. Mech., 12, 193 (1932).   † N.A.C.A. Tech. Mem. 1046 (1943).
‡ Proc. Phys. Soc., 61, 352 (1948).

Cavity Formation on Impact

As the body penetrates the liquid it leaves an air cavity behind it, the lines which form the boundary of the cavity leaving the body (tangentially if it is a sphere) to make a cone of angle about 18° (cf. Fig. 67, Plate II). In the cavity stage a sphere has a drag coefficient equal to 0·33, less than that of the fully submerged sphere at moderate Reynolds numbers owing to the absence of turbulent wake, but more than at low Re (stream-line flow) owing to the absence of back pressure.

The shape of the cavity suggests that as the ball cleaves the liquid it imparts momentum to it in such a way that the velocity of the water outwards is initially a constant fraction of that of the projectile. As the walls of the cavity move out, at the same time the hydrostatic force gives the water an acceleration inwards until the cavity closes up at a waist and then breaks up into a mass of small bubbles.

Resistance in Cavity

If a sufficiently high frequency of photography is used it is possible to plot the displacement : time curve of the projectile after it has formed a cavity and so calculate its resistance in motion. At high entry speeds the frictional resistance is the paramount force causing deceleration. If M is the mass of the projectile, d its diameter, V its speed, ρ the density of the liquid:

$$M\frac{\partial V}{\partial t}=Mg-c_D\cdot\frac{1}{2}\rho\,V^2.\pi\frac{d^2}{4}\quad.\quad.\quad.\quad.\quad.\quad(73)$$

where c_D is a drag coefficient which relates the frictional force to the projected area of the projectile and the pressure at its front stagnation point in the conventional fashion.

This may be written, when ρ' is the specific gravity of the solid in terms of the liquid and s the path traced by the sphere:

$$\frac{\pi d^3}{6}\cdot\rho'\left(g-V\frac{\partial V}{\partial s}\right)=c_D\cdot\frac{\pi}{8}\cdot d^2V^2$$

When the speed and deceleration are such that the effect of gravity can be neglected, we have for the drag coefficient

$$c_D=3\cdot05\frac{d}{s}\rho'\log_{10}\frac{V_0}{V}$$

V_0 being the entry speed to water, V that after path s.

Since (73) can be written (at sufficient speeds to make the weight negligible)

$$\frac{\partial V}{\partial t}\cdot d=CV^2$$

where C is a constant for a given solid and liquid, it is evident that this type of motion can be scaled on a basis of proportionality between acceleration $\partial V/\partial t$ and V^2/d, i.e. on a Froude parameter. This implies a geometric scaling of cavity shapes. Hydrostatic forces will scale on the same basis, but, strictly speaking, the density of the vapour filling the cavity should change in proportion, though as it plays a small part in the flow pattern this is an academic point. Departure from a Froude scaling will occur after the cavity has closed and the speed is reduced, for then gravitational forces become important and with reduced Re, c_D is no longer constant for a particular shape. The scaling still applies even when the projectile enters at supersonic speeds—for the liquid; only it is preceded by shock waves in the liquid (McMillen*).

Cavitation

True cavitation is a phenomenon which occurs when the pressure on parts of a projectile travelling at high speed through a liquid is reduced so low that a vacuum (or at any rate a region saturated only with the vapour of the liquid) is formed. Again, in terms of Bernoulli's theorem, in motion when gravity can be ignored

$$\rho \frac{\partial \phi}{\partial t} + \rho \frac{U^2}{2} + p = \text{constant}$$

cavitation will ensue where p is reduced to the vapour pressure. In unsteady motion $\partial \phi / \partial t$ can be large and cavitation take place without much increase of U. Those shapes of body causing the largest accelerations in the flow—namely at sharp corners—will cavitate at the lowest mean speeds of propulsion. When p_0 is the pressure in the undisturbed flow, the factor $(p - p_0)/(\frac{1}{2}\rho V^2) = K$ is called the cavitation number; the smaller K is, the more likely is a cavity to form.†

Although evidence of cavitation first appears near sharp shoulders of the body it does not necessarily occur at the solid boundary itself, but often a little way out in the cores of incipient vortices. Zones of local separation also develop minute eddies in the boundary layer in which cavitation can occur. As K decreases, the rate of evaporation increases, and a cavity once started will grow till it develops all but the fore portion of the obstacle. The impact cavities which described in the preceding section must be considered from their shape to correspond to $K=0$ in spite of the presence of air in the cavity.

On a convex surface such as that of a sphere, cavitation may ensue where the pressure drops to a minimum and afterwards recovers (cf. Fig. 16), at first in a fine-grained structure resembling soapsuds in appearance. For a given shape when fully submerged, fully developed cavitation and separation in the boundary layer occur at about same place, although on the sphere, as we have noted, the pressure in a wind-tunnel reaches the static value at latitude 45°, whereas the lines of flow

* *Phys. Rev.*, **68**, 198 (1945).
† The usual symbol is σ, but K is used here to avoid confusion with the symbol for surface tension.

$K=0$ leave the body at latitude 65° (cf. Fig. 16 and Fig. 67). Cavitation is, in fact, first apparent a little downstream of the place of minimum pressure on a body.

The stream-lines for a sphere in a stationary cavity, i.e. one in which the walls remain steady and do not, as in practice, collapse, were derived by Bauer* by combining a source with a uniform streaming in the direction of motion and removing the portion of the field in the wake. The surface of discontinuity formed by cutting out this portion of the field has to conform to the wetted portion of the solid and, further back, to the cavity wall. It is unable properly to fulfil both conditions since its shape is really a paraboloid, but a rough approximation may be made to the flow by this means. If the flow is made to leave tangentially at 65°, it does not quite fit at the front stagnation point (Fig. 68). Bauer adjusted the potential pattern so that the fluid left the sphere at an azimuth,

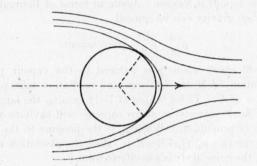

Fig. 68.   Derivation of cavity form by potential functions.

reckoned from the front stagnation point, of 50°, whereas in practice this angle is nearer 65°.

The potential and stream functions are:

$$\phi = U(r \cos \theta + a^2/r)$$
$$\psi = U(\tfrac{1}{2}r^2 \sin^2 \theta - 2a^2 \sin^2 \theta/2)$$

The line $\psi=0$, which has to be fitted to the sphere, is given by $\cos \theta/2 = a/r$ and touches only at the front stagnation point. To make this stream-line touch at 50° we require $\cos \theta/2 = 1 \cdot 1 a/r$ (cf. Fig. 68). Bauer found by integration of the pressure over the cap, $c_D = 0 \cdot 15$ instead of the experimental $0 \cdot 3$. Taylor obtains a better fit by using a suitable distribution of sources in place of the single one, and so derives $c_D = 0 \cdot 27$ for a wetted cap extending from $\theta_0 = 0°$ to 65°.

Observations of this phenomenon and of the drag associated with it are made in a cavitation tunnel. This is a "circus" filled with water from which as much air as possible has been removed by pumping into a partial

* *Ann. d. Physik*, **82**, 1014 (1927).

vacuum which overlies the return half of the circuit. By means of piezo-electric pressure gauges over the surface of a model it is possible to measure the pressure distribution during cavitation. The total drag can also be measured on a force balance.

Fig. 69 shows the variation of drag coefficient with cavitation number for a cylinder with hemispherical head and streamlined tail, its axis being *parallel* to the stream. (The Reynolds number is of order 10^5.) The value for $K=0$ cannot be derived from the experiments on this model, since the tunnel has not a sufficient maximum speed, but the value of c_D for a sphere at impact on water, in the cavity stage, has been inserted at $K=0$ and the curve extrapolated (dotted) to this value to show that it fits in quite well, as we have already suggested (p. 97). The reader will appreciate that at this stage of fully developed cavitation the shape of the tail in the bubble has no influence on the drag, so that we may treat this model in the cavitation tunnel as though it were just a sphere. Drag

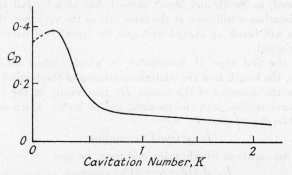

Fig. 69. Variation of drag coefficient with cavitation number.

in the cavity stage is in fact nearly all profile drag, there being no wake in the accepted sense.

Break-up of Liquid Jets

When a jet of liquid issues from a nozzle into the atmosphere, the jet eventually breaks up into drops under the action of disturbances of its equilibrium figure. The jet is observed to break up at a point which can be determined accurately as long as the pressure behind the nozzle remains constant.

In the main there are two types of break-up. In the first the interplay of inertia and surface tension results in the jet becoming varicose. Rayleigh* examined the conditions under which axial-symmetrical oscillations set up near the nozzle might increase in amplitude. In an inviscid jet he showed that a disturbance having a wavelength 4·4 times

* *Proc. London Math. Soc.*, **10**, 4 (1879).

the diameter of the jet should grow fastest and eventually break up the jet into drops (Fig. 70, Plate II). He subsequently modified his theory to take account of the viscosity of the liquid, which naturally reduces the rate of growth of the optimum disturbance, whose wavelength in relation to the diameter of the jet remains unchanged.

In the second type of disturbance, the jet becomes sinuous and the resistance of the air to the passage of the humps becomes of more importance than surface tension (Fig. 71, Plate II).

Since the air resistance to this type of motion increases rapidly with speed, break-up will occur at a faster rate as the speed of efflux is increased, whereas the varicose form of disturbance has a rate of growth independent of the speed of efflux. When a liquid jet enters the air, both types of disturbance are equally possible, but at low speeds the varicose form will break up the jet first. Since the growth coefficient of the "optimum" wavelength is constant, the continuous length of the jet will be proportional to the speed, as Smith and Moss* showed, but at a critical speed the sinuous disturbance will grow at the same rate as the varicose; thereafter sinuosities will break up the jet first and the length will decrease with increasing speed.

Taking the first type of disturbance, in which surface tension predominates, the length L of the continuous portion of the vertical jet may depend on the diameter of the nozzle, D; the density of the liquid, ρ; its interfacial tension with the medium, gas or liquid, which surrounds it, σ; and on the velocity, V. Let

$$L = \rho^x D^y \sigma^z V^n \times \text{constant}$$

Equating exponents of length, mass, and time, we find

$$L = \rho^{n/2} D^{1+n/2} \sigma^{-n/2} V^n \times \text{constant} \quad . \quad . \quad . \quad (74)$$

But experiment shows that L is directly proportional to V for a given jet (cf. Fig. 72), so set $n=1$ and

$$\frac{L}{D} = V \sqrt{\frac{\rho D}{\sigma}} \times \text{constant} \quad . \quad . \quad . \quad . \quad (75)$$

On the other hand, as we have suggested, at higher velocities the sinuous type of disturbance may be expected to predominate and for this we shall take the Reynolds number VL/ν as pertinent, i.e. L inversely as V. That this is so is shown by the experimental results of Smith and Moss, and others (see the curve for rubber solution, Fig. 72). The critical velocity at which the jet length is a maximum involves, then, both surface tension and viscosity, and separates a straight section and a hyperbolic portion of the length : velocity characteristic. The straight portions of the curves for all jets from circular nozzles can be made to coincide [as (75) indicates] if L/D be plotted against $V\sqrt{(\rho D/\sigma)}$. This has been done for "thin" (i.e. not very viscous) liquids on Fig. 72.

* *Proc. Roy. Soc.*, **A93**, 373 (1917).

PLATE II.

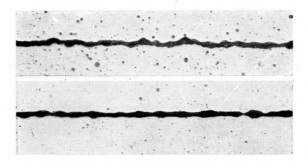

Fig. 70 (top) and Fig. 71 (bottom). Break-up of liquid jets.

Fig. 89. Ripple formation in sand.

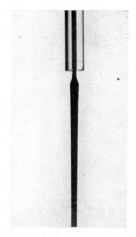

Fig. 67. Cavity formed on impact of sphere with liquid.

Fig. 97. Relaxation of elastic fluid on emergence from capillary tube.

Agreement is also found with the same formula when the liquid debouches into a reservoir of another liquid with which it does not mix. The only departure from (75), as far as the straight sections of the curves go, occurs when the jet is of mercury or a very viscous material like rubber solution or glycerine. Large viscosity delays the break-up and produces longer jets than in moderately viscous liquids, other things being equal.

If a liquid jet enters a reservoir of a liquid with which it forms no interface or if a gas jet enters a gas, the interfacial tension between gases being negligible, only the sinuous disturbance is possible and the relation between length to the breaking-up point and speed of efflux is hyperbolic

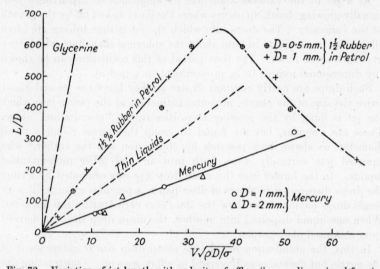

Fig. 72. Variation of jet length with velocity of efflux (in non-dimensional form).

throughout. This is the genesis of the "sensitive jet" or "sensitive flame."

Formation of Drops

We have omitted to mention a stage of the $L : V$ characteristic curve for a jet which precedes the straight portion. This is a region of such slow efflux that the jet bulges into incipient drops as soon as it leaves the nozzle; as though the surface film formed a bag hanging from the nozzle which filled up with liquid and then became detached, or at any rate was linked by a narrow neck to the next "bag" to be filled. This stage is more notably developed when the jet is allowed to trickle on to a plate at a short distance from the nozzle. If the distance between nozzle and plate is carefully adjusted, remarkable bulges appear on the surface, giving it a corrugated appearance. Where the stream is bounded by a surface of curvatures r_1 and r_2, a pressure excess equal to $\sigma(1/r_1 + 1/r_2)$ is built up on the inside of the boundary. Under these circumstances Bernoulli's equation takes the form

$$\rho g h + \sigma \left(\frac{1}{r_1} + \frac{1}{r_2}\right) + \frac{1}{2}\rho V^2 = \text{constant}$$

At any level below the nozzle, a balance must ensue between V (or $Q/\pi a^2$) and r_1 and r_2, the outflow Q remaining nearly constant. A family of curves may be drawn for any initial values of the curvature of the surface and the radius a of cross-section. Curves constructed in this way agree quite well with experimentally observed shapes.

As a jet in the varicose state has its amplitude of disturbance continually growing, break-up occurs where the jet is nicked off by the growth of the varicosity. The drops into which the jet is then broken are often ellipsoidal, but oscillate in form about the spherical shape into which they at length settle down. The time period of this oscillation can be shown (by dimensional means) to be proportional to $\sqrt{(\rho a^3/\sigma)}$.

Such drops are nearly constant in size as they leave the jet and about twice the size of the nozzle, in contradistinction to the pieces into which the jet is flung by the growing sinuosities in the "atomisation" stage. These are irregular, but are found to group themselves round a mean diameter, as shown in a research by Merrington and the author,[*] who squirted jets vertically down both into air and other (non-miscible) liquids. In the former case the mean drop size was estimated by letting the drops disperse on to sheets of filter-paper, a previous experiment with single drops having shown how the stain size varied with drop diameter. When one liquid dispersed into another, the mean drop size was derived from measured photographs.

In this, the atomisation region, the mean drop size is independent of the nozzle but decreases as the speed of efflux goes up. Constructing the parameter for the drop in the form Vd/ν—where ν is the kinematic viscosity of the liquid forming the jet—and plotting it against ν/ν_0, the relative viscosities of the two media, one obtains a relationship which, for jets in air, is approximately $(Vd/\nu)^{\frac{1}{5}} = 500$.

Fall of Drops

The rates of free fall of drops of water have been determined by Laws photographically, the size being found at the end of their path.

Lenard[†] and Laws[‡] determined the rate of free fall of water drops, collecting them for size as above (except that Laws preferred to let them fall on to flour and to weigh the pellets of dough so formed). The larger drops, of course, experience a drag involving the formation of an eddying wake, whereas the finer ones have a velocity conditioned by Stokes' law. The data are shown in a table and on Fig. 73.

* *Proc. Phys. Soc.*, **59**, 1 (1947).   † *Met. Zeits.*, **39**, 249 (1904).
‡ *Trans. Amer. Geophys. Union*, **3** (1941).

d (mm.)	0·10	0·20	0·30	0·40	0·50	0·60	0·70	0·80
V (m. per sec.)								
Stokes	0·33	1·32	2·95	5·3	8·2	11·8	16·0	21·2
Actual	0·33	1·15	1·75	2·2	2·8	3·4	4·0	4·6

d (mm.)	1·0	1·75	3·0	4·0	5·0	6·0	8·0	10·0
V (m. per sec.)								
Actual	4·7	5·9	8·2	8·8	9·3	9·3	Unstable	

When the drops are fine and have a considerable distance to fall their radius diminishes due to evaporation.

At the same time that it is falling the drop loses mass by evaporation. Actually a balance ensues between the diffusion of molecules from the drop into the vapour surrounding it and those which condense into the drop. If the boundary layer of molecules is not swept away by convection this is purely a problem in diffusion for which Langmuir* has derived the formula

$$-\frac{ds}{dt}=\frac{4\pi M.D}{\rho RT}p = k'\frac{p}{T}$$

where s=surface of drop, M=molecular weight, R=

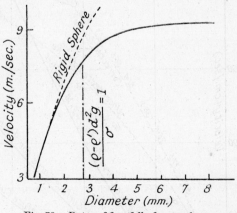

Fig. 73. Rates of free fall of water drops.

gas constant, D=diffusion coefficient, T=absolute temperature, ρ=density of liquid, and p its saturation vapour pressure.   Inserting the appropriate values for water we find the following values for the rate of evaporation, ds/dt.

TEMPERATURE	p/T	ds/dt cm.^{2} per sec.
0° C.	27·5	$1·4\times10^{-5}$
10° C.	35	$2·5\times10^{-5}$
20° C.	41	$4·5\times10^{-5}$

(An experimental value for water at 15° C. is 3×10^{-5} cm.^{2} per sec.)

It is evident that over the range of terminal velocity for which Stokes' law holds, every drop suffers a constant deceleration (due to evaporation) whatever its size, while its temperature remains constant.   Thus for small raindrops at 10° C. this deceleration is 3 cm. per sec.^{2}.

* *Phys. Rev.*, **12**, 368 (1918).

Langmuir's equation does not contain any term covering convective evaporation, i.e. no term involving the speed of the drop through the atmosphere into which it is evaporating. The rate of evaporation is in fact a function of Reynolds number. This has been proved experimentally by Frössling,* who held water drops on glass threads in a small wind tunnel and measured the rate of decrease of mass at various wind speeds.

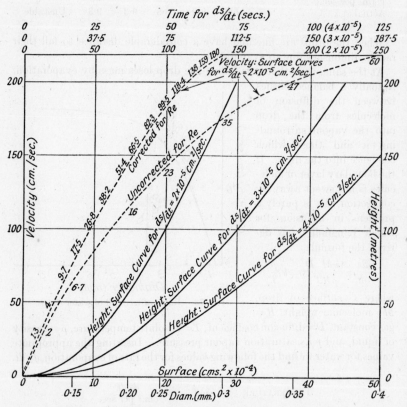

Fig. 74. Fall and evaporation of drops; height : surface curves.

He found that the right-hand side of Langmuir's equation must be multiplied by

$$\left(1+\frac{0\cdot276\sqrt{Re}}{\sqrt[3]{(D/\nu)}}\right)=(1+0\cdot1\sqrt{Re})$$

for water at 20° C.

Armed with these data we can trace the change in size and speed of fall of a drop as it falls at any constant temperature. The dotted curves on Fig. 74 show the relationship between terminal velocity and surface

* *Beit. z. Geophysik*, **52**, 170 (1938).

(or r^2) for a given rate of evaporation (ds/dt). These are deduced by reversing the drop's path and assuming it starts from nothing at ground level and has its surface increased with height by a constant amount for every 10 seconds of its life (cf. time scales at top of figure). This gives us the right-hand dotted curve, but owing to convectional evaporation the life-time of a droplet is reduced, in other words, we must correct this curve by calculating values of Reynolds number at various epochs—these are shown alongside the curve—and moving each 10 seconds point to the left so that, for instance, an increment of surface 2×10^{-4} cm.^{2} takes place in $10/(1+0\cdot1\sqrt{Re})$ seconds instead of in 10 seconds just. The corrected velocity : surface curve is the left-hand dotted one.

Starting from ground-level it is then possible to calculate by steps the height at which a drop will have a given surface (or size) if its life history is reversed. These heights are marked (in metres) alongside the corrected curve. Height : surface curves can then be plotted. Several of these are shown on the figure (as full lines) for three values of ds/dt. If a drop possesses a definite size on hitting the ground instead of being evanescent, as we have assumed, it is only necessary, in order to apply the graphs, to assume the ground to be raised to meet it by the corresponding amount. Thus, if $ds/dt=3 \times 10^{-5}$ cm.^{2} per sec. and the drop is $\frac{1}{4}$ mm. diameter on hitting the ground (i.e. remnant surface 20×10^{-4} sq. cm.), "ground-level" must be pushed up 50 m., or else 50 m. subtracted from all heights on the scale to the right of the figure.

The author* made some measurements on the fall of water drops in an enclosed tower nearly 50 m. high. Drops were allowed to fall from a fine burette and their "initial size" was measured by photography 10 cm. below the mouth of the burette. Their time of fall to the bottom of the tower, where they were caught on blotting-paper, was measured by chronometer. The water was dyed so that from the size of the stain—after a preliminary calibration—the "final size" of the drop could be deduced. Drops of a saturated solution of zinc chloride were also used. The reduction of size with height confirmed that deduced theoretically above.

Limiting Drop Size in Free Fall

It was postulated at the commencement of this section that disruption of the jet at high speeds is controlled by viscous and inertia forces. At lower speeds the varicose disturbance would be the dominant cause of break-up, while an intermediate type of break-up, in which the jet followed a sinuous motion, also occurs. We should therefore expect the relationship deduced from the above-mentioned experiments to cease to apply at low velocities. The varicosities then break the jet up into ovoid lumps which eventually resolve into drops comparable with the jet diameter and therefore with the nozzle diameter. Below the limiting velocity, the drops

* *Proc. Durham Phil. Soc.*, **10**, 394 (1946).

from narrow jets become, for a given liquid, uniform in size, so that the scatter of drop size disappears. With fine nozzles (1 mm. diameter) the constant drop size reached at low velocities is roughly twice the nozzle diameter, with all but the very viscous liquids. This is in agreement with some figures obtained from an examination of photographs of varicose jets included in a paper by Tyler.*

LIQUID	NOZZLE DIAMETER (mm.)	DROP DIAMETER d (arbitrary units)	JET DIAMETER D (arbitrary units)	RATIO d/D
Water . . .	{0·65	22	10	2·2
	{0·45	20	10	2·0
Aniline . . .	{0·45	19	8	2·3
	{0·60	16	7	2·3
Mercury . .	0·30	36	20	1·8
			Mean	2·1

When jets issue from *large* nozzles at low speed, the drops are not found to be uniformly twice the diameter of the nozzle. This is because large drops falling through the air are unstable, dividing up into smaller units to an extent dependent on the path of fall and therefore on the distance of the collecting apparatus from the nozzle.

A drop of liquid in motion through another fluid differs in its behaviour from a solid sphere in that it may (a) be deformed, (b) have a circulation set up within itself by the shearing effect of the relative motion of the two fluids. These effects upset the stability of the drop, causing it to oscillate about the spherical shape and eventually to burst into fragments or at least into smaller drops.

Before bursting, the effects of deformation and circulation become apparent as an increase in the resistance, compared to that of a rigid sphere of the same diameter (cf. Fig. 73). Bond and Newton† investigated this effect and showed that the parameter relevant to these changes was $(\rho - \rho')d^2 g/\sigma$, where ρ and ρ' are the densities of drop (or bubble) and medium respectively. The value of this "Bond number" (B) was of the order unity when the rate of fall began to change. Such a value of B applied to air bubbles rising slowly in liquids; for liquid drops in a liquid medium it was higher—up to 5 in some cases. (The value $B=1$ for water drops has been indicated on Fig. 73.) A few experiments (unpublished) have been done by Davies on the size of drops which will break up in the last 10 ft. of their fall when released from heights of 30 to 40 ft. It appears that deformation ensues when B exceeds 0·4 and circulation within the drop becomes effective when $B=1·5$. As these results are rather meagre and refer to small heights, it was thought

* *Phil. Mag.*, **16**, 504 (1933).   † *Ibid.*, **5**, 704 (1928).

desirable to make use of a tower of greater height (125 ft.) in the interior of which the drops were let loose. The drops were formed by aspirating some of the liquid up a graduated glass tube of between 1 and 4 mm. diameter and launching it by suddenly reversing the pressure applied to it. In this way drops up to 1 cm. diameter can be produced entire, although, since they are not initially spherical, a certain amount of oscillation about the equilibrium form occurs before they settle down. In falling they are watched through a telescope at the top of the tower and the height at which they break up, if that occurs, is calculated roughly by timing from release.

As the drops fell, they acquired an oscillation of figure which grew in amplitude until, if not stopped by the filter-paper at the bottom of the tower, they broke either into two or three pieces or else into a remaining drop of moderate size surrounded by a chaplet of tiny drops. The diameter of each drop was measured by its initial volume and checked by the diameter of the stain it produced. It was not possible to reproduce conditions exactly. Drops of the same size and liquid did not always break up at the same place in their fall, nor, if near the critical size, did both necessarily burst before reaching the bottom.

By plotting d^2 against $100\sigma/\rho g$, that value of d (in millimetres) was noted which best represented the critical size; hence the critical Bond number was deduced.

LIQUID	$\dfrac{100\sigma}{\rho g}$	d^2	d from 125 ft.	B	d^2	d from 50 ft.	B
			(mm.)			(mm.)	
Dirty water . . .	5·0	50	7	10	95	10	19
Distilled water . .	7·3	100	10	14	100	10	14
Carbon tetrachloride	1·6	13	3·6	8	28	5	18
Tetrabromethane .	1·55	16	4	10	25	5	16
Methyl salicylate .	2·7	42	6·5	16	50	7	19
Ditto (thickened) .	2·9	72	8·5	25	80	9	28
Glycerine+20 per cent. water .	5·5	78	9	14	100	10	18

The mean values of B for "thin" liquids are 17 and 12 for 50 and 125 ft. respectively. The fact that a larger drop remains entire at the smaller height can be ascribed to the shorter time over which the disrupting forces can operate. The viscous liquid—thickened methyl salicylate—shows exceptionally high values of the critical B. This indicates a superior resistance to the tendency of shearing forces to produce circulation and is paralleled by Bond and Newton's observations of viscous oil drops in water.

To summarise this part of the work on drops; at low velocities a change in the type of break-up may limit the mean size of drop attainable from a jet and in such a case the mean size will no longer be independent of the diameter of the nozzle In addition, the maximum drop size will in any type of break-up be limited by the size of the largest drop which can remain unbroken under the circumstances, even at high velocities and particularly with large nozzles.

CHAPTER 6

FLUIDS SHOWING ANOMALOUS VISCOSITY: SUSPENSIONS

So far we have dealt with fluids which are homogeneous in the sense that the fluid is only present in one phase and has no adulterant in the form of discrete particles or specks of other matter or of another phase of its own matter present in it. When such specks do exist, especially when they are solid grains dispersed through the continuous fluid phase, the speckled system is called a suspension. Although the material forming the continuous phase must be fluid, the suspended material may be solid, liquid, or gas. Such disperse systems may be further classified as "sols" or "gels." In a sol there is no connecting link between the dispersed particles as a whole, although individual pairs may coalesce or single ones be subdivided on collision. In a gel there is a structure which binds the whole mass together as by a framework which envelops the continuous phase.

We shall in this chapter consider those systems of the first class which have no rigidity (i.e. flexural elasticity), though they may show compressibility (i.e. bulk elasticity). Whereas sols flow in the general sense that they are unable to resist indefinitely the application of an external force, they do not behave in the same way as homogeneous fluids. Generically they are called "non-Newtonian," or said to possess "anomalous viscosity." Their flow properties also depend on the relative concentration of the suspended particles, their shape, and size.

Mechanical Analysis

One of the most important processes to which the physicist submits a suspension is that by which he determines the relative numbers of particles falling within certain size limits. This, for instance, is a factor in determining that elusive quality of the soil which the farmer calls "tilth"; in the ceramic industry it serves to differentiate those clays which are suitable for making such diverse products as face-powder and paper. An analysis of this type applied to wind-borne dust and river-borne silt of cities may enable the origins of possible pollution to be traced, while to the geologist it forms a basis of the science of pedology.

Now to describe the method by which a mechanical analysis of a sol is usually made. The particles are allowed to settle under gravity in a tall cylinder and it is assumed that they do so under Stokes' law, i.e. that they shortly attain a terminal velocity proportional to the square of their diameters. If, now, a "sample" is taken at a depth h after a time t

from the commencement of sedimentation, the "weight"—using the word in no literal sense—of the sample will be proportional to the number of particles in the suspension having velocities $<h/t$, i.e. to Σnd^2, where the summation extends from particles so small as to remain permanently in suspension up to those having the given terminal velocity. If the sampling is continuous, the curve so obtained is a summation curve (Fig. 75—continuous line), whose slope plotted against d (Fig. 75—dotted line) gives the required size : frequency curve.   The two curves are related in the same way as the summation and distribution curves of statistics, and in simple types the second curve bears a close resemblance to the normal error curve of Gauss.

Many methods have been devised to do the necessary sampling. Pipette or hydrometer insertions at intervals give the curve step by step.

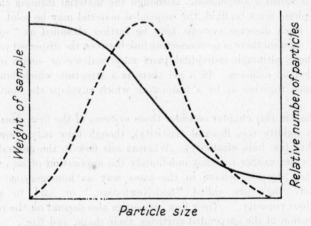

Fig. 75.   Summation and distribution curves of particle size.

In the apparatus devised by the author,* the assessment of the relative numbers of particles at different depths is done continuously by a narrow beam of light which passes athwart the tank containing the liquid at a given height and falls on a photo-electric cell connected to a galvanometer. The extent to which the photo-electric current differs from that recorded when no particles are in the way of the beam is a measure of the "weight" —in the statistical sense—of the solid at the place and instant in question. Before the results obtained can be interpreted it is of course necessary to have a relation between grain size and light absorption.   This calibration is carried out by using particles all of the same known size in the liquid and then repeating the measurements with other sizes and concentrations. The record of current against time at a fixed depth while the solid settles in an actual suspension of mixed particles proves in fact to be an actual

* Proc. Phys. Soc., 55, 48 (1943).

summation curve like that shown in Fig. 75. A similar shaped curve may be derived by working with constant time and variable depth. In this case it is necessary to take a silhouette of the whole settling tank and to analyse the negative for blackness by passing it gradually through a narrow beam of light falling on the photo-electric cell. The advantage

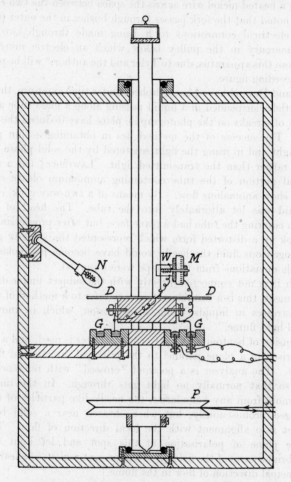

Fig. 76.   Hot-wire coaxial cylinder viscometer.

of the photo-electric method is that the analysis takes place continuously and not by steps and that no interference with sedimentation is involved by dipping in pipettes or hydrometers to take samples.

Now we return to a discussion of the flow of suspensions. The measurement of the point-to-point velocity in flow may be made in two ways, by means of a hot-wire or visually. We have earlier discussed the possibilities of using the cooling of a thin hot-wire in pure liquids as a measure of velocity. In suspensions this is more difficult owing to the tendency of the solid particles to clog the wire. Nevertheless, the feat may be accomplished, and Fig. 76 shows a Couette viscometer with a means of traversing a heated nickel wire across the space between the two cylinders. It will be noted that the fork passes through bushes in the outer (rotating) cylinder, electrical connections to it being made through two annular pools of mercury in the pulley below which an electric motor turns. Results from this apparatus, due to Tyler and the author,* will be presented in the succeeding figure.

Pichot and Dupin† have photographed, under time exposure, the motion of the particles suspended in a liquid passing along a glass tube and from the length of streaks on the photographic plate have deduced the velocity gradient. The success of the method lies in obtaining a thin pencil of brilliant light and in using the light scattered by the solid phase to affect the plate rather than the transmitted light. Lawrence‡ fed a dye into the central portion of the tube containing ammonium oleate solutions, known to show anomalous flow. By means of a two-way cock, clear and dyed liquid was let alternately into the tube. The head of the dye portion on entering the tube had a plane face, but after progressing a little way it took up a distorted form which represented the velocity gradient. In a homogeneous fluid the heads would have become parabolas, but in the colloids deviations from this shape were observed.

[Though it is not connected directly with the subject under discussion at the moment, this is a suitable occasion to refer to a method of studying shearing stresses in liquids, using a suspension, which is known as a "polarised light flume."

A suspension of bentonite (0·2 per cent.) in water is used, and a beam of light polarised in a plane parallel to the principal direction of flow sent athwart it. The analyser is a polaroid "crossed" with reference to the polariser so that normally no light gets through. In the main fluid stream remote from any boundaries, the needle-like particles of the solid are arranged promiscuously, but when sheared near a solid boundary will be set into alignment with the local direction of flow. This will rotate the plane of polarisation at this spot and let light through. Thus the bright parts of the field of view represent regions of shear relative to the principal direction of flow in the flume.]

Velocity Gradient in Suspensions

A number of suspensions of rice starch in paraffin were prepared and tested in the concentric cylinder apparatus. Fig. 77 shows results in an

---

* *Proc. Phys. Soc.*, **45**, 142 (1933).   † *Comptes Rendus*, **192**, 1079 (1931).
‡ *Proc. Roy. Soc.*, **A148**, 59 (1935).

11 per cent. concentration at several rates of rotation of the outer cylinder, together with one (broken line) for pure paraffin. In consequence of the variation of η with velocity gradient [cf. (19), p. 12] these lines have a marked curvature compared with that of the homogeneous liquid, pure paraffin. If the moment on the inner cylinder is measured this is no longer in linear relationship to the speed of rotation of the outer one, as

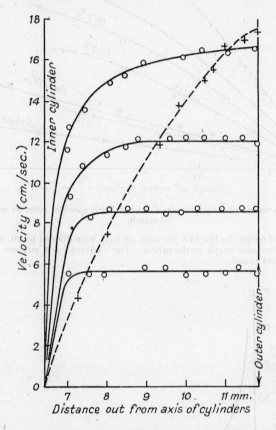

Fig. 77.   Velocity gradients of suspension in coaxial cylinder viscometer.

it should be in Newtonian flow [cf. (18), p. 12], but shows a diminishing viscosity as the rate of shear increases (Fig. 78). This torque is proportional to the velocity gradient at the inner cylinder, or $M/(r^2 \partial\omega/\partial r)$ is a (relative) measure of the viscosity. One can derive the corresponding values of velocity gradient and shearing moment, M, from Figs. 77 and 78 to get proportional values of η such as those on Fig. 79, where one can see how η diminishes with increasing velocity gradient, or rate of shear,

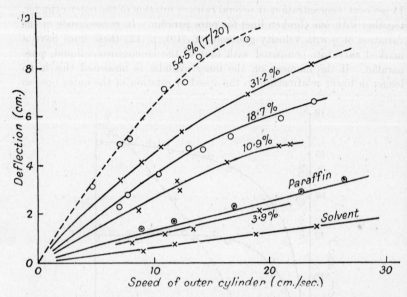

Fig. 78. Variation of torque on inner cylinder with speed of outer in suspensions of starch.

The values of torque for the 54·5 per cent. sol have been divided by 20, in order to exhibit it on the same graph as the others. The "solvent" is a mixture of carbon tetrachloride and paraffin.

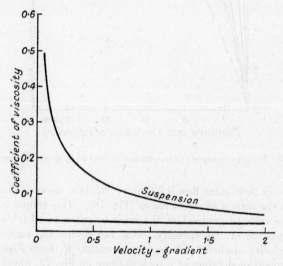

Fig. 79. Variation of viscosity of suspension with velocity gradient; the horizontal line being that of the pure solvent.

At sufficiently high values of the latter, in fact, the viscosity comes down to that of the continuous phase of liquid.

In a viscometer in which the overall effect and not the point-to-point velocity gradient is measured, it is usual to equate the ratio of shear stress at the walls to the mean rate of flow and to call this the "apparent viscosity" whose value will change for a given suspension from one instrument to another. The true viscosity in such an apparatus, of course, varies from one stratum of fluid to the next. It is possible, working backwards, to assume some simple law connecting the true viscosity with the

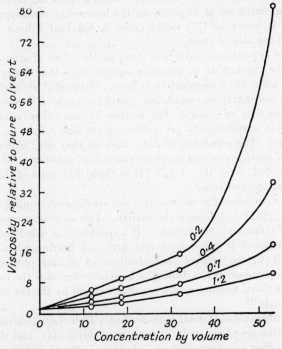

Fig. 80. Variation of viscosity of suspension with concentration.

velocity gradient, e.g. to take log η/η_0 inversely proportional to $\partial U/\partial r$ as Fig. 78 suggests, and to see how this fits the observed relation between shear stress and outflow in the viscometer concerned.

Fig. 80 shows the variation with concentration of η/η_0 for the rice starch suspensions—as derived from curves like those of Fig. 77 with 78— for selected values of the velocity gradient (numbers attached to curves). This variation of viscosity with concentration has been a subject of theoretical interest to a number of workers, beginning with Einstein.*

* *Ann. d. Physik*, **19**, 289 (1906).

They concur in a formula of the type:

$$\eta_s = \eta(1 + kc\bar{e}) \quad \quad \quad \quad \quad \quad (76)$$

in which η_s is the viscosity of the suspension, η of the pure liquid, c the mass concentration of the solid, e its specific volume. k is 2·5 for spherical particles, according to Einstein, but is subject to the subtraction of a function of the ratio of length to breadth in ellipsoidal or needle-like particles. It will be noted that the theory takes no account of variation of viscosity with velocity gradient; indeed, (76) can only be tested in the light of data such as those of Fig. 80, of which all that can be said is that, up to a concentration of 30 per cent., the increase of viscosity with concentration is linear, as (76) would make it, but that k must also be a function of the rate of shear.

Very few experiments have been done on the effect of size of particle on viscosity, though it is generally agreed that this factor becomes important when the concentration is large. Sakurada* showed that, for the same concentration, needle-like particles made a suspension less viscous than one of spheres, but neither he nor other workers have centrifuged a suspension to get uniform grain size before making flow experiments. The consensus of data, such as they are, indicates little influence of particle size and shape on anomalous viscosity until the paste stage is reached, when the "liquid" is so thick that some of the features of solid friction supervene.

If smaller particles of submicroscopic size are dispersed among the larger ones they appear to lubricate the matrix. This is of importance in the yielding of quicksands to pressure. If a quicksand is dried and the fine particles removed it becomes in fact firm and bearing when water is added to it to the original concentration. A similar phenomenon of practical importance in the drilling of bore-holes for oil is the conferment of lower frictional resistance between drill and soil by the use of colloidal "drilling muds."

When a suspension of solid particles has a high concentration relative to the continuous phase, as in a paste, a moulding clay, and the like, it exhibits another property, that of "plasticity," the ability to withstand to a certain degree the application of forces tending to make it flow. The substance then ceases to be fluid in the strict sense of the word, but since flow does take place slowly after a critical stress has been exceeded, it is advisable to say something of such systems here.

The critical stress below which no motion takes place is often known as the "yield value," and suspensions which, after a critical stress has been exceeded, flow at a rate proportional to the *excess* rate of shear are called, after their discoverer, "Bingham bodies." (It must be noted that such bodies should not be called "Newtonian above the yield value"

* *Koll. Zeits.*, **64**, 195 (1933).

since, although the graph of flow against rate of shear is a straight line (Fig. 81), it does not pass through the origin and the coefficient of viscosity as defined (p. 3) is not a constant.)

More often, this graph is not a straight line but bends over towards a limiting viscosity at high rates of shear, just like less concentrated suspensions. With some it may even increase, so-called "dilatant materials."

Plug Flow

When a substance exhibits a yield value, we can, following Buckingham,* write the equation of flow in a capillary tube as

$$\eta \frac{dU}{dr} = S - S_0 = \frac{\partial p}{\partial x} \cdot \frac{r}{2l} - S_0$$

(cf. (16), p. 12)

where S is the actual stress and S_0 the critical stress below which no flow takes place. At a given value of

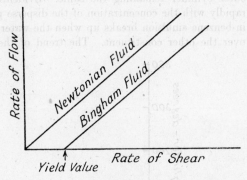

Fig. 81. Characteristic curves of true fluid and Bingham body.

$\partial p/\partial x$ a gradient of velocity will only be found where $r > 2Sl/(\partial p/\partial x)$, the central portion inside this moving *en bloc* (Fig. 82). The sheath outside may be regarded as a lubricant between this central plug and the wall of the tube. Scott-Blair and Crowther† showed that such plug flow was common to clay and soil pastes of sufficient concentration.

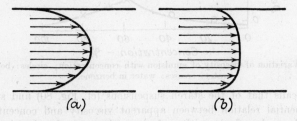

Fig. 82. Velocity distribution in a tube; (a) normal flow, (b) plug flow.

Emulsions

Another class of dispersed system which shows interesting behaviour under stress is that of emulsions, in which both continuous and discrete phases are liquid. The author‡ made some measurements on the behaviour of these systems when subjected to shear in a concentric cylinder apparatus,

* J. Amer. Soc. Testing Materials, 1154 (1931).   † J. Phys. Chem., 33, 321 (1929).
‡ Koll. Zeits., 65, 32 (1933).

using water and benzene as the two components.   By adding a little sodium
oleate to the water and shaking it up with the benzene the latter appears
in the emulsified form, whereas if magnesium oleate be added to the
benzene and shaken up with water it is the latter which is dispersed in
drops.   Fig. 83 shows how the torque communicated to the inner cylinder
depends on the concentration in both types of emulsion, the speed of the
outer cylinder remaining the same.   Evidently the viscosity increases
rapidly with the concentration of the disperse phase, although the water-
in-benzene emulsion breaks up when the water predominates in quantity
over the other constituent.   The trend of the other curve (benzene-in-

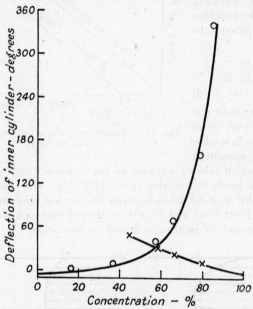

Fig. 83.   Variation of viscosity of emulsion with concentration; circles: benzene in
water; crosses: water in benzene.

water) recalls that of the starch suspensions (cf. Fig. 80) and suggests
an exponential relation between apparent viscosity and concentration.
In fact, if one plots the logarithm of η/η_0—where η is the viscosity of the
emulsion and η_0 that of the "solvent"—against concentration one obtains
a straight line (Fig. 84).   Broughton and Squires* have found that the
viscosity of emulsions decreases as the rate of shear increases, their data
following a curve like that of Fig. 78.

If an increase of pressure δp acts on a substance of volume v to reduce
it by δv, the compressibility is defined as $\delta v/v . 1/\delta p$.   This is a constant
for a given material as long as elastic laws are obeyed.   In the same

* J. Phys. Chem., 42, 253 (1938).

way we can think of an increase of the space occupied by the disperse phase by an amount δc as reducing the average separation of the discrete globules by the fraction $\delta l/l$, so that $-\delta l/l \cdot 1/\delta c = \chi$ where χ is a sort of "interphasal" compressibility, whose value depends on the relative compressibility of the two phases or, in colloquial terms, on the over-crowding of the disperse phase which is resisted by the continuous phase. When flow takes place we can think of the continuous medium having to move between obstacles of average separation l and in doing so being subject to a viscous resistance denoted by the coefficient η. If over-crowding reduces the separation of the impedimenta to $l-\delta l$, the viscous

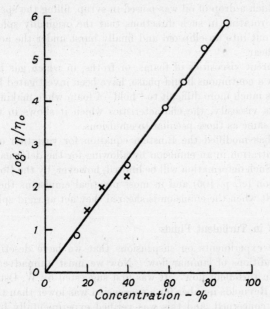

Fig. 84.   Variation of viscosity of emulsion with concentration.

resistance must increase in the proportion of η to $\eta + \delta\eta$.   Therefore

$$\frac{d\eta}{\eta} = -\frac{dl}{l} \times \chi \cdot dc$$

The solution of this equation is $\eta = \eta_0 e^{\chi c}$, or in logarithmic form, $\log(\eta/\eta_0) = \chi c$.

This formula, tested against the results of the author and those of other workers, who measured the apparent viscosities of such emulsions as albumen and blood, gives good agreement with theory, having regard to the fact that most of the available data refer to *apparent* viscosity, derived from torque measurements in concentric cylinder viscometers. The suspensions satisfy a similar law if one regards in their case χ as a function of the rate of shear and not a constant for the two phases involved; but the work needs repeating with regard to uniformity of drop size in the emulsion.

G. I. Taylor* has studied the flow of emulsions from the point of view of stability and has obtained an expression for the upper limit to the size of drop which can subsist while the fluid is being sheared. The conservative force is the interfacial tension between phases while the disruptive force is the pressure difference between the inside and the outside of the drop caused by the viscous forces; both of these depend on the radius of the drop. He has also carried out some illuminating experiments in which a drop of oil was poised in syrup, filling the space between four rollers rotating in such directions that the originally spherical drop was pulled out into an ellipsoid and finally burst under the action of the excessive shear.

The apparent viscosities of foams, or froths, in which gas bubbles are dispersed in a continuous liquid phase, have been investigated by Sibree.† Though it is much more difficult to "hold" a foam while making measurements of its viscosity, the characteristics which it shows in flow are in general the same as those peculiar to emulsions.

Taylor‡ has modified the Einstein equation for variation of viscosity with concentration in an emulsion by allowing for the deformation of the droplets. Such deformation will be limited, however, by the Bond number of the motion (cf. p. 106) and in most practical emulsions the drops are so small that when the emulsion is sheared they act as rigid spheres.

Suspensions in Turbulent Fluids

All these experiments on suspensions that we have described so far refer to conditions of laminar flow. Now we must animadvert on their behaviour in turbulent flow. It was first suggested by W. Ostwald§ that the critical Reynolds number for a suspension was lower than that for the pure liquid concerned, and this was verified experimentally by Andrade and Lewis,‖ who found, using a transparent concentric cylinder viscometer, that turbulence set in when a sol was in the apparatus at about three-quarters of the peripheral speed of the outer cylinder required for turbulence in pure water, the flow being made visible by submerged aluminium particles.

A study of the behaviour of suspensions in fully developed turbulence is important in connection with the flow of rivers loaded with silt and of sand in sand-storms. Emulsions are also manufactured commercially by letting strata of two liquids flow together through a flume in turbulent motion so that mixing occurs and one becomes dispersed in the other.

* *Proc.. Roy. Soc.*, **138**, 41 (1932).   † *Trans Farad. Soc.*, **30**, 325 (1934).
‡ *Proc. Roy. Soc.*, **146**, 501 (1934).   § *Koll. Zeits.*, **36**, 99 (1925).
‖ *Koll. Zeits.*, **38**, 261 (1926).

Hurst* first showed that if a suspension of sand were placed in a jar of water and the whole stirred into turbulence, each size grade distributed itself in the jar according to an exponential law of increasing concentration with depth. In an actual stream, whether a river or a small model canal, the equilibrium at a level y, where the silt density is maintained at a mean value c by the motion, may be formulated thus:

$$Bc + A\frac{dc}{dy} = 0 \qquad \ldots \ldots \quad (77)$$

where B is the velocity of free fall of the particles (cf. p. 24) and A is the austausch coefficient (p. 45). The austauch coefficient, or eddy viscosity ν', can be determined from the concentration gradient at any level, dc/dy, and as ν' is also equal to $l^2 \,|\, dU/dy \,|$, by (35) and (36), a comparison of concentration with the velocity gradient will enable one to determine the variation of mixing length across any section of the canal.

The author tested the equation (77), repeating Hurst's own measurements but using the optical method (p. 50) for estimating values of c at different levels y in a glass-sided vessel holding 3 litres of water and a 1 per cent. suspension of sand. Six small propellers interspersed with baffles (on one side of the jar only) stirred up the suspension in turbulent motion; a narrow beam of light traversed the other side of the vessel at various heights, and the light fell on a photo-electric cell; the illumination being measured in terms of the current through the latter. If $n=$the number of grains intervening, $I_0=$the light intensity after traversing pure water, $I=$the intensity after passing through the suspension

$$n \propto \log \frac{I_0}{I}$$

if the ordinary laws of light absorption are obeyed. Further, if Hurst's exponential law is obeyed

$$\log \frac{n_0}{n} = \frac{B}{A} y$$

On Fig. 85 the results of these experiments are plotted, in the form $\log n_0/n$ against h, for different (average) grain sizes. The fact that nearly straight lines are obtained confirms the assumption that the light absorbed is, with sufficient accuracy for these experiments, proportional to n. The linearity fails at great depths, intimating departure from one or both of the above laws. That it is more likely the second than the first which fails may be judged from the reasoning developed later, pointing to abnormal concentrations near the bed. A decrease of specific gravity naturally diminishes B/A (cf. the lines for the fuller's earth).

The author† then set out to study the transport of a sediment formed of, as nearly as possible, spherical grains of uniform size and specific

---

* *Proc. Roy. Soc.*. **A124**, 196 (1929).

† *Phil. Mag.*, **17**, 769 (1934); *Proc. Roy. Soc.*, **162**, 583 (1937).

gravity, forming the loosely compacted bed of a channel in which flow of water in either laminar or turbulent flow could take place. Thus, in a given experiment, the velocity gradient at the bed was the principal variable. This was measured by a hot-wire anemometer, while the silt density was measured optically by the method already described (p. 50). The experiments took place in a glass-sided channel of section 18 in. square and working section 8 ft. long. The first material employed for the sediment was fuller's earth of specific gravity 1·6 and mean particle diameter 0·05 mm. It was necessary to choose a fine, light material of this nature if measurements of erosion and silt transport under stream-line

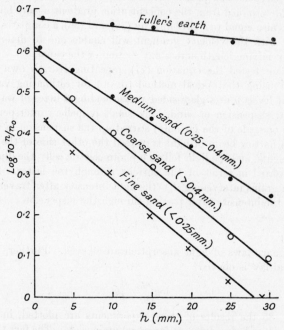

Fig. 85. Distribution of silt density with depth.

conditions of flow in a water channel were to be observed. Fig. 86 shows the velocity gradients over the bed at three (average) speeds. At the lowest (circles) no appreciable erosion took place; at the medium speed (St. Andrew's crosses) transport of the silt was beginning, though the water flow was still laminar; at the highest speed (Latin crosses) general turbulence had intervened and the bed was being rapidly carried away. The velocity gradient in a suspension is usually steeper at a boundary in a suspension than in a homogeneous liquid (cf. p. 113). The anomalous viscosity of systems such as these undoubtedly adds another difficulty to the testing of any theory of erosion.

In an actual river the grains are lifted near the bottom by the Magnus effect (p. 10) since they lie in a region where, owing to the gradient in the boundary layer, the velocity on their undersides is less than on top. The smaller ones are then held permanently in suspension by the turbulent

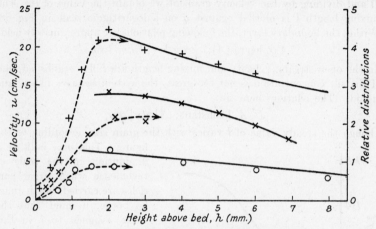

Fig. 86.   Velocity gradients in silt-loaded channel.

motion, but the larger ones fall back after rising above the zone in which the velocity gradient is paramount, till they are lifted up again. The path of the grains in this "saltation zone" is cycloidal, that of a succession of jumps. Similar effects occur in the lee of a sand-dune, but of course

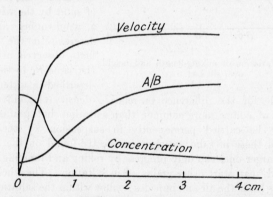

Fig. 87.   Velocity, silt density, and austausch in silt-loaded channel.

for a given degree of turbulence the sand grains do not rise so high, size for size.

Fig. 87 shows, for sieved sand falling in the grade 0·25-0·3 mm., the distribution of velocity U, concentration of sand c, and the values of A/B

from equation (77) with height above the bed of the glass-sided water channel. In each case, after a small and nearly constant value through the mobile portion of the bed, the austausch reaches a constant value a few centimetres above the bed. Multiplying by the appropriate value of B and dividing by the velocity gradient we obtain the value of l^2. The mixing length l is plotted against y on a logarithmic scale in Fig. 88. Within the boundary layer, the following relations are approximately held:

$$U \propto \log(y+1); \quad c \propto y^{-1}; \quad A \propto y, \; l \propto y$$

In the open stream, velocity and mixing length are fully established, and if the silt concentration is not too great, the system behaves like a true liquid. The relations here are:

$$U, A, l \text{ constant}; \quad |\log c| \propto y$$

though the steady value of l varies with the grain size, according to the

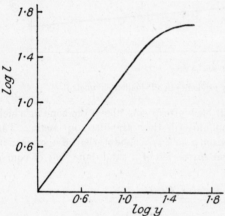

Fig. 88.   Variation of mixing-length and height over silt bed.

figure. This may indicate a diminution in the scale of turbulence when larger particles are carried, but it must be borne in mind that the value assigned to l in this region depends on that of B.

Formation of Sand-dunes and Sand Ripples

Bagnold* has made extensive studies of the transport of sand by the wind, both in a wind-tunnel and in the desert. In the model the facts observed are similar at the same Re to those already described in water, allowance being made for the difference in relative density of solid and liquid. Rolling is of course more common than saltation, but grains up to 0·2 mm. may be carried permanently in suspension by the prevailing winds, and these in calm weather are mostly found on the tops of the dunes. Larger ones can only progress by rolling and jumping, and where they "land" can start other grains off in saltation. The whole assembly of particles loads the air and impedes its flow within the saltation zone to a much greater extent than in a river, as is shown by the estimated values of the drag coefficient in the two cases. Above this zone the velocity rises logarithmically, as if within it the mobile sand constituted a rough surface (cf. p. 47). The characteristic ripples in the sand correspond to

* *Proc. Roy. Soc.*, **A157**, 594 (1936).

the mean length of a jump, so that their length diminishes as the mean grain size d increases.

Under water the ripples in the sand, which are left high and dry when the tide recedes (Fig. 89, Plate II), are more often produced by a laminar to-and-fro motion of the water relative to its bed—another form of periodic boundary layer (cf. p. 39). Bagnold* has found in this case that the ripple pitch (or wavelength) increases at first with the amplitude of the water motion up to a limit at which it remains constant and proportional to d. If, as in his experiments, the floor of the channel is oscillated, the particle velocity at any height ξ is given by (32), p. 40, which reduces to the first term at large values of $\sqrt{(\omega/2r)}.\xi$, showing that, in view of the small value of ν in water, the damped motion does not extend far from the bed and most of the water moves *en bloc* relative to it. Within this sheared layer, however, the velocity gradient has amplitude $C\omega^{3/2}/\nu^{\frac{1}{2}}$ by (32).

Taylor, in an appendix to Bagnold's paper, expresses the rate of shear $\partial U/\partial y$ in a parameter $\Gamma=[\partial U/\partial y]_{y=0}.d^2/\nu$ and then equates the resistance of the particle to the buoyancy:

$$\rho\left[\frac{\partial U}{dy}\right]^2 d^4 f(\Gamma)=(\rho-\rho')gd^3$$

This gives $f(\Gamma)$ in terms of $\rho-\rho'/\rho.gd^3/\nu$. The undetermined function, according to the experimental evidence, is proportional to the $\frac{2}{3}$ power of the latter quantity.

Substituting for $|\partial U/\partial y|^2$, we then derive

$$\omega\propto\left[\frac{\rho-\rho'}{\rho}\cdot\frac{g\nu}{C^2d}\right]^{\frac{1}{3}}\cdot\left[\frac{gd^3}{\nu^2}\right]^{\frac{2}{3}}$$

The critical value of ω to start grains moving was actually found to vary inversely as the $\frac{3}{4}$ instead of the $\frac{2}{3}$ power of C.

Landsberg and Riley† have since made similar measurements in the wind over sand-dunes. They suggest that one could measure the strength and frequency of gusts from simultaneous wind speed and sand sampling over the dunes. From their results they also worked out $\sqrt{(u^2)}$ as a "scale of turbulence" at various heights and found it practically independent of elevation but proportional to the mean U at a standard reference height.

Fundamental Aspects of Erosion

Erosion is a problem of considerable complexity which cannot readily be expressed in terms of known physical laws. Up to the present it has lain mainly in the sphere of the engineer, who has evolved a number of empirical laws for predicting its magnitude. It is evident by the disagreement not merely in coefficients but even in the functions on which the erosion is made to depend that these rules are designed only to fit the conditions which fall within the experience of particular engineers and

* *Proc. Roy. Soc.*, **A187**, 187 (1946). † *Univ. Iowa Bull.*, 342 (1942).

have no universal application. Before further progress can be made one must attempt to reduce the problem to its simplest proportions. Pioneer fundamental research in the subject was carried out by Gilbert,* while more recently Hjulstrom† in Sweden and the author‡ in this country have independently carried out laboratory and field experiments in which the variable quantities have been reduced to a minimum. The factors which then remain can be grouped under two headings: first, those which concern the eroding stream—whether it is in steady motion or turbulent, and in particular the value of the gradient of stream velocity at the surface of the soil; second, the nature of the soil bed—the size, shape, and density of the grains and whether they are closely or loosely compacted.

In field experiments all these factors intervene in a fashion which does not allow of the separation of their respective contributions. It is desirable, as a basis for establishing the laws of erosion, to make experiments first in artificial channels, as described in the preceding section. If, then, one plots the height against the logarithm of the silt concentration, one obtains a line which is almost straight (except near the bed) whose slope can be taken as a measure of the erosion coefficient (cf. Fig. 85). For a given velocity gradient, provided the stream is sufficiently turbulent to afford adequate mixing, this coefficient is found to be inversely as the grain size, bearing out theory in this respect.

Similar considerations apply in natural streams, where the bed, of course, is not homogeneous. Samples taken out of a river in flood at various depths and analysed in respect of size-frequency give a series of curves whose mean slope for each size follows the same distribution. The only exception, occasionally reported by hydraulic engineers who measure in terms of surface velocity and slope of bed, is that "colloidal" particles are less easily eroded than somewhat larger ones, so that in a mixed bed there is maximum rate of erosion occurring for a diameter round about 0·1 mm. This anomaly is usually attributed to the superior cohesion which clay sludge possesses. The exception, however, disappears if one reckons the erosion in terms of the velocity gradient. It is well known that the distribution of velocity across a stream carrying finely divided or colloidal material is not the same as that in homogeneous fluids or in those in which large crumbs of sparsely distributed soil are in suspension (p. 113).

Probably the most important factor in loosening the bed prior to actual erosion is the extent to which it allows permeation by the fluid. When water passes over the soil a certain amount of chemical action may take place, particularly when the surface soil is a limestone formation; but whether this occurs or not, once the water is able to break up the soil into smaller crumbs or to encompass those which already existed before its passage, it can exert pressure to move the formerly coherent grains,

* *U.S. Geol. Survey*, Paper 86 (1914).   † *Bull. Geol. Inst. Upsala*, **25**, 221 (1935).
‡ *Loc. cit.*, p. 121.

which then become potential silt. Sometimes an actual lifting force may be exerted; that is to say, the line of action of the pressure may be inclined upwards instead of along the bed. This happens notably when a grain is lying a little higher than its fellows on the bed and its foundations are partially or completely undermined by the fluid. The local velocity at the top of the grain is then greater than that beneath, so that the force towards the underside may exceed the total of gravity and the downward force on the top. Such a state of affairs often occurs where a pebble is resting on a sandy bottom and may lift it momentarily into the body of the stream. As soon, however, as it has risen above the boundary layer of fluid in which the major part of the gradient of velocity is found, the lift is lost and it sinks back. This accounts for the series of long hops by which the heavier particles follow the stream and the ultimate formation of ridges or dunes (cf. p. 124), but this process does not, in the writer's observation, contribute markedly to the silt load of the stream itself, which is a function merely of the degree of turbulence, velocity gradient, and grain size. Penetration of the soil by the eroding fluid can, nevertheless, change the distribution of velocity near the bed—in fact, at a sandy bottom the gradient of velocity may show a point of inflexion separating the domain of quasi-fluid motion above and quasi-solid motion below—and in this way react on the silt load carried in suspension.

Emulsions in Turbulent Flow

As suspensions in turbulent flow have more technical importance than ones in which the motion remains laminar, so with emulsions. These are, in fact, made commercially first as coarse dispersions by the atomisation of jets, as described in the preceding chapter, and then in a further process these are broken down under the action of turbulence. In the latter process the chance of coalescence has to be considered, although this can be discouraged by the addition of an emulsifying agent (like soft soap) to the continuous phase. Clay* has examined the behaviour of originally coarse emulsions in a turbulent field, both in a transparent channel at Re approximately 10^5 and in a coaxial cylinder apparatus like that of Andrade and Lewis in the super-critical stage. Photographs disclosed the following features: (a) nearly all drops were spherical, the actual division or recombination process rarely being caught by the camera; (b) a number of droplets seemed to be in contact without coalescence, especially small ones clinging to a larger like an offspring to its mother; (c) at this Re the size–frequency curves have their maxima at 10 microns (diameter). Homogeneity of the emulsions was promoted by high volume concentration of the dispersed phase and high Reynolds number, but the difficulty in securing a homogeneous emulsion is that factors which promote bursting also promote coalescence by bringing droplets more often in contact, so that there is a limit to the smallest mean particle size attainable.

* *Proc. Roy. Acad., Amsterdam*, **43**, 852, 979 (1940).

CHAPTER 7

ELASTIC LIQUIDS

Sol–gel Transformation

Certain types of liquid which exhibit anomalous viscosity like sols also show elasticity in virtue of a structure which knits the disperse phase together in a framework filled with cells of the continuous liquid. These are known generically as "gels" and often derive from or become converted into sols by a change of temperature, by agitation, or by chemical action in the process called peptisation. A foam where the cells are filled with

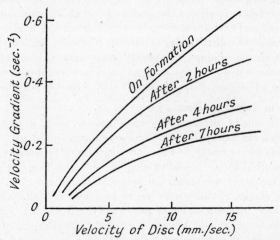

Fig. 90.   Velocity gradients during setting of gel.

gas may also be elastic. Two types of elasticity may be shown, bulk elasticity (really a form of compressibility) or flexural elasticity ("rigidity"); these involve resistance to change of size or of shape respectively.

The sol–gel transformation may be illustrated by making up a solution of leaf gelatine or glue in warm water to a concentration of about 1 per cent. If a horizontal suspended disc be set in motion in it and the velocities of flow which it induces when so doing be plotted at different epochs during cooling, curves like those of Fig. 90 result.* In normal viscous flow without radial motion these would be straight lines. Actually the initial one is nearly so, but as time goes on anomalous viscosity sets

* *Trans. Farad. Soc.*, 29, 494 (1933).

in, shown by the increasing curvature of the gradients; at the same time the increased extent to which the sol is being dragged with the disc, exemplified by the general reduction of the gradients, tells us that the average viscosity is increasing while the sol sets to a gel. Just before complete gelation the observations had to be given up, for lumps of the jelly would cling as more or less rigid masses to the disc until, after a few more revolutions, they would relax.

Another feature of the gelation process, viz. the acquirement of elasticity, may be illustrated on the same apparatus if the disc is uncoupled from the motor and given an impetus to turn it. In the first stages of the sol–gel transformation the motion of the disc is dead-beat and it comes slowly to rest. As the viscosity grows, the time to come to rest decreases, but the inception of gelation is signalled by a swinging to and fro of the disc before it reaches equilibrium. This stage marks the development of elasticity in the substance.

When a liquid has this interwoven structure—whether in a micro-cosmic form and visible under moderate magnification as in glues and jellies, or whether due to the form of the molecules as in rubber solution—it exhibits rigidity, so that if a small shear is applied to it, it deforms to a certain extent, but on release of the stress recovers. The recovery in the case of elastic fluids is usually partial only, complete recovery being a property of an elastic *solid*, and although some concentrated gels like a stiff culinary jelly show complete recovery, they can scarcely be said to flow in the usual sense. If too large a stress is applied, the structure may break down, the liquid becoming a sol and losing its rigidity. Sometimes this transformation is permanent or it may only be temporary, the gel re-forming when the stress is removed. This last is a case of "thixotropy," *vide infra*.

The Relaxation Theory of Viscosity

Maxwell* supposed that every fluid possesses a certain amount of elasticity. If the coefficient of elasticity be multiplied by a time factor there results another coefficient having the dimensions of viscosity. On this view the application of shearing stress to a substance produces a strain of value dependent on the elasticity (E) and this strain disappears at a certain rate determined by a characteristic time (τ) called "time of relaxation." The product of these quantities has the dimensions of viscosity. Thus in a normal oil both E and t are small, but in an oil paint τ is con-siderable, while E remains small, conferring anomalous viscosity and rigidity. If, on the other hand, τ is small and E is large we have the gel, which can have the same viscosity as the sol, although it behaves so differently, if the product of E and τ is the same for each. From this aspect, the increase of viscosity in a sol at high concentrations and low

* *Phil. Mag.*, **35**, 133 (1868).

rates of shear is to be ascribed to a rise in relaxation time. This again, following Hatschek,* we may attribute to electrical adsorption of the liquid by the particles of the pigment, which lose some of this protective sheath as the velocity gradient increases. This view is borne out to a certain extent by the observations of Eirich, Bunzl, and Margaretha,† who found no anomaly in the flow of a suspension of electrically neutral particles—spores of the puff-ball *lycoperdon*—dispersed in a mixture of paraffin and tetrachlorethane.

The velocity gradient in a gel may be regarded as made up of two parts, one due to the force acting on unit area and expressed as F/η; the other in phase with the *rate of change* of force acting on unit area and expressed as $(dF/dt)/E$. (On the nature of E we shall say more presently.) The difference between the two contributory terms is well brought out when the gel is subject to simple harmonic displacement of the type already illustrated (p. 125). If the force is expressed in the form $fe^{i\omega t}$, where ω is the pulsatance of the forcing, the velocity gradient becomes:

$$\frac{\partial U}{\partial y}=\left(\frac{1}{\eta}+\frac{i\omega}{E}\right)f \quad \text{or} \quad \eta\frac{\partial U}{\partial y}=(1+i\omega\tau)f \quad . \quad . \quad (78)$$

The velocity gradient has then two components, one in phase with the applied force and one at $\tan^{-1}(\omega\tau)$ to it and varying with the frequency. In the case we are picturing, the force would be a shear, and the strain a change of shape.

On the other hand, one may think, as Philipoff‡ does, of an alternating *compression* and *distension* of the material whose *size* is thereby changed. If, then, the displacement of the centre of mass of the system is $S=se^{i\omega t}$ the equation of motion is

$$\frac{dF}{dt}+\frac{F}{\tau}=Ei\omega S$$

while F executes S.H.M. with an amplitude

$$\frac{E\omega S}{\sqrt{(1+\omega^2\tau^2)}}$$

The quantity in the denominator may be regarded as the viscous impedance which the system offers; the fluid acts as though it had a complex viscosity of value:

$$\eta=\frac{\eta_0}{\sqrt{(1+\omega^2\tau^2)}} \quad \bullet \quad \bullet \quad \bullet \quad \bullet \quad \bullet \quad (79)$$

At low frequencies the viscosity is η_0 simply, but as the frequency of the compressive force increases, the viscosity falls (especially in the neighbourhood of $\omega=\tau^{-1}$). Philipoff tried this expression on gels, but established better agreement of the experiments with an exponent $\frac{3}{4}$

* *Koll. Zeits.*, **9**, 280 (1912).   † *Koll. Zeits.*, **74**, 277 (1936).
‡ *Phys. Zeits.*, **35**, 885 (1934).

of $\omega\tau$ in the denominator of (79). τ was about 0·01 second for a 10 per cent. gel.

Here are some other specimen values of relaxation time: pitch, at 30° C. (130 seconds); sulphur melt at 120° C. (3 seconds); hexane 7 parts and methanol 3 parts at 30° C. (0·7 second); 4 per cent. viscose (0·004 second).

It should be pointed out that τ is not necessarily a constant for each material; it may vary with stress amplitude and is certainly changed by breakdown of structure.

Schofield and Scott-Blair* have shown that Maxwell's ideas can be applied satisfactorily to flour dough, and although this material is to be classed as a plastic solid rather than a fluid, their conclusions are instructive in our present topic. They find that owing to a lag in recovery from elastic strains a factor $d\epsilon/dt$ must be subtracted from the elastic term in the equation of motion, expressed in this case as de/dt, where e is the fractional elongation of a baton of dough under a stretching force P per unit cross-sectional area. Thus

$$\frac{de}{dt} = \left(\frac{1}{E}\frac{dP}{dt} - \frac{d\epsilon}{dt} \right) + \frac{P}{\eta}$$

This term, representing the "elastic after-effect," is large after abrupt strains, but otherwise small during the application of a stress.

Maxwell's equations have also biological importance in connection with the stretching of muscle, which is a substance showing elastic and viscous behaviour, complicated by "recovery," staleness, and other factors involving chemical reactions not shown by dead matter.

Elastic Liquids under Shear

Since viscosity is really a result of submitting a fluid to shear, a better picture of the relaxation of a gel is to be obtained by submitting the liquid to an alternating shear, as the author did in the experiments during the sol–gel transformation described at the beginning of this chapter. These have since been extended† to study the behaviour of a settled gel in a cylindrical vessel which is given simple harmonic motion about a central vertical axis so that an alternating torque is applied to the liquid. Beside the viscosity, elasticity in the guise of the modulus of rigidity comes into play, the latter being defined as the ratio of shear stress to shear strain, apparent as the development of velocity gradient.

Two cases will be considered.

Case A. The liquid, in the form of a column extending along the y axis, is given an oscillatory torque $\theta = \theta_0 e^{ipt}$ over the face $y=0$. If N is the appropriate modulus of shear (rigidity), η the coefficient of viscosity, and

---

* *Proc. Roy. Soc.*, **A141**, 72 (1933).   † *Phil. Mag.*, **36**, 473 (1945).

ρ the density, the equation of motion for an annulus δr wide and δy thick at radius r and depth y is:

$$2\pi r^3 \delta r \partial y \rho \frac{\partial^2 \theta}{\partial t^2} = 2\pi r^3 \delta r \delta y \left(N \frac{\partial^2 \theta}{\partial y^2} + \eta \frac{\partial^3 \theta}{\partial^2 y . \partial t} \right)$$

or

$$\frac{\partial^2 \theta}{\partial t^2} = \frac{N}{\rho} . \frac{\partial^2 \theta}{\partial y^2} + \frac{\eta}{\rho} \frac{\partial^3 \theta}{\partial^2 y . \partial t} = c^2 \frac{\partial^2 \theta}{\partial y^2} + v \frac{\partial^3 \theta}{\partial^2 y . \partial t} \quad \cdots \quad (80)$$

and the solution for waves travelling up and down the column:

$$\theta = C e^{(\alpha + i\beta l)} [e^{(\alpha + i\beta)(y-l)} - e^{-(\alpha + i\beta)(y-l)}] e^{ipt} \quad \cdots \quad (81)$$

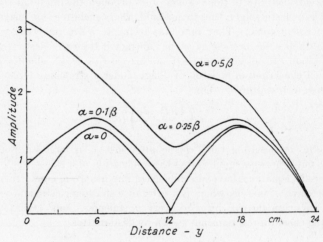

Fig. 91.   Amplitudes in visco-elastic fluid; axial case.

when a rigid barrier prevents movement at $y=l$. The amplitude at any level y in terms of that at the base is given by:

$$\theta_y{}^2 = 2\theta_0{}^2 [\cosh \{2\alpha(y-l)\} - \cos \{2\beta(y-l)\}] \quad \cdots \quad (82)$$

Substituting (81) in (80) we find

$$(\alpha^2 - \beta c^2)(c^4 + v^2 p^2) = -p^2 c^2; \quad 2\alpha\beta(c^4 + v^2 p^2) = -vp^3$$

or

$$\alpha^2 = p^2 \left[\frac{\sqrt{(c^4 + v^2 p^2)} - c^2}{2(c^4 + v^2 p^2)} \right]; \quad \beta^2 = p^2 \left[\frac{\sqrt{(c^4 + v^2 p^2)} + c^2}{2(c^4 + v^2 p^2)} \right]$$

[If $v=0$, $\alpha=0$, $\beta=p/c$; if $c=0$, $\alpha=\beta=\sqrt{(p/2v)}$.]

The function θ/θ_0 is plotted on Fig. 91 for $l=24$, $\beta=2\pi/24$, and values of α equal to 0, 0.1β, 0.25β, 0.5β. The first case gives the usual stationary wave distribution of amplitude. The others show pseudo-nodes whose position begins to deviate from the first and at which the minimum amplitude gets greater with α/β.

Case B. The sides of the column are given an oscillatory torque—the same throughout the column—and waves are propagated radially. The equation of motion is now:

$$2\pi r^3 \delta r \delta y \rho \frac{\partial^2 \theta}{\partial t^2} = N\left(2\pi r^3 \frac{\partial \theta}{\partial r}\right)\delta r \,.\, \delta y + \eta \frac{\partial}{\partial r}\left(2\pi r^3 \frac{\partial^2 \theta}{\partial t \,.\, \delta r}\right)\delta r \,.\, \delta y$$

or $\qquad \dfrac{\partial^2 \theta}{\partial t^2} = c^2\left(\dfrac{\partial^2 \theta}{\partial r^2} + \dfrac{3}{r}\dfrac{\partial \theta}{\partial r}\right) + \nu\left(\dfrac{\partial^3 \theta}{\partial r^2 \,.\, \partial t} + \dfrac{3}{r}\dfrac{\partial^2 \partial}{\partial r \,.\, \partial t}\right) \qquad$ . . (83)

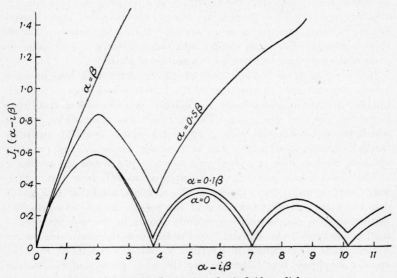

Fig. 92. Amplitudes in visco-elastic fluid; radial case.

If we substitute $\theta = \phi e^{ipt}$, ϕ being a function of r alone,

$$\frac{\partial^2 \phi}{\partial r^2} + \frac{3}{r}\frac{\partial \phi}{\partial r} + \left(\frac{p^2}{c^2 + ip\nu}\right)\phi = 0$$

or $\qquad \dfrac{\partial^2 \phi}{\partial r^2} + \dfrac{3}{r}\dfrac{\partial \phi}{\partial r} + (\alpha - i\beta)^2 \phi = 0$ . . . . . (84)

The solution of this may be obtained in terms of Bessel functions of complex argument[*] as $\phi = [J_1 r(\alpha - i\beta)]/[r(\alpha - i\beta)]$. The function $J_1(\alpha - i\beta)$ is plotted on Fig. 92 for values corresponding to those of Fig. 1. Those for $\alpha = 0$ and β are available in the tables of the Bessel and the *ber* and *bei* functions; the others have been calculated as series from the formula,[*]

$$J_1(\alpha + i\beta) = \sum_{m=0}^{m=\infty} J_{(1+m)}\alpha \,.\, J_m(i\beta)$$

[*] See, for example, McLachlan's *Bessel Functions for Engineers*; Lamb's *Hydrodynamics*, §357.

In the experiments about to be described, it is the modulus of the linear displacement amplitude at each radial distance in the liquid which is actually measured. The angular amplitude at the same place is θr. Thus the curves of Fig. 92 give the theoretical distribution of amplitude through the liquid, measuring from the centre outwards when $p/c=1$.

The purely elastic fluid therefore shows nodal circles at the appropriate resonant frequencies of oscillation. A liquid having elasticity and viscosity exhibits pseudo-nodes and antinodes as in case A. When the liquid has an overwhelming viscosity, the amplitude at any radial distance falls off steadily from the edge towards the centre, there are no pseudo-nodal circles, but this does not mean to say that the liquid moves *en bloc* as there is a progressive phase change with radial distance so that different parts of the fluid may be moving in opposition of phase.

In the experiments a metal bowl 22 cm. diameter with upright sides 10 cm. deep formed the container of the liquids, which were: diesel oil, cellulose acetate in acetone sols, and gelatine in water sols of small concentration (up to 6 per cent.). The container was mounted on a table which, through connecting rods to an electric motor, could be oscillated through various small angles and at constant frequency. In order to simulate the condition A a fixed ring was held just inside the container so that disturbances could not be propagated inwards from the moving walls, only upwards from the base. To simulate condition B a guard disc was fixed just above the base of the vessel. It will be noted that neither of these experiments corresponds exactly to the two-dimensional motion assumed in the analysis. In the first case the guard ring causes a diminution of amplitude in its vicinity, but it was noticed that the angular amplitude was constant over the main portion of the surface where the measurements were made. In the second type of experiment the guard disc imposed an overall zero amplitude at the base, but did not affect measurements made in the vicinity of the free surface. It did not, in fact, prevent a distribution closely resembling that of Fig. 92 in the body of the liquid being set up, the disturbing effect being confined to a centimetre above the guard disc. These regions were avoided in placing the anemometer about to be described.

As the introduction of recording devices having bulk and inertia was undesirable, it was decided to use a hot-wire anemometer. A nickel wire 1 mil. diameter and 1 cm. long was soldered to a fork formed of two steel needles which could be located at any position in the liquid, being mounted as it was on a micrometer for traverse either along a radius of the tank (the wire itself being vertical) or parallel to the axis of the tank (the wire then lying along a radius) for the B and A cases respectively.

An alternative method of studying the elastic constants of the liquid is to measure the pseudo-wavelength by employing two hot wires at a distance along a radius (B) or vertically over each other (A) and recording the phase difference between the oscillations in potential (at double the applied frequency) across them. For this purpose, tappings from each wire were led to the *X* and *Y* pairs of plates of a cathode-ray oscillograph and the relative positions of the wires adjusted until an easily recognisable Lissajous figure—straight-line or ellipse—was drawn by the electron spot on the screen.

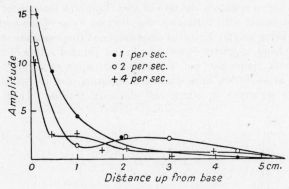

Fig. 93. Amplitudes in Diesel oil.

As the thermal lag of the hot wire varies with frequency (cf. p. 82) it was necessary to calibrate the indications of the hot-wire recorder over a range of frequency and amplitude covering that to be used in the experiments. This was done for each liquid by mounting the hot-wire fork on the connecting rod of a reciprocating motor which carried it to and fro

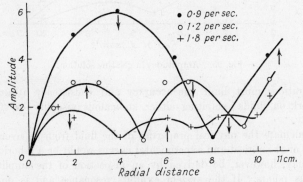

Fig. 94. Amplitudes in cellulose acetate.

in simple harmonic motion in the liquid. The measured potentials are nearly proportional to the square roots of the amplitudes.

Experimental plots of displacement amplitude and of places in and out of phase are given in Figs. 93, 94, 95 for diesel oil having no elasticity, for cellulose acetate in acetone with viscous and elastic properties of the same order of magnitude, and for gelatine solutions in which the elastic structure overrides the viscosity.

On comparing these with Figs. 91 and 92, we observe a general agreement in the shape of the curves. Some discrepancy may be ascribed to experimental inaccuracy, but a major difficulty in all work with sols and gels is that the effective viscosity varies with the rate of shear. Since it is impossible to maintain the rate of shear constant throughout the fluid we should expect such variations, the deduced value of the coefficient of viscosity being greater when the amplitude and frequency are small. On the other hand, a greater consistency in the deduced values of the elastic moduli with frequency and amplitude are apparent, though another difficulty arises herein since continued agitation of a gel tends to break down the structure to which the elasticity is due. These physical

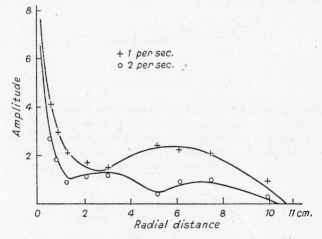

Fig. 95. Amplitudes in gelatine solution.

considerations must limit the accuracy and consistency attainable in any work on fluids exhibiting either anomalous viscosity or structural elasticity.

To calculate the physical properties of the fluid from an overall comparison of theoretical and experimental curves would be a laborious task. They may, however, be derived by an inspection of the amplitudes at judicious points. If the system exhibits resonance and is not highly viscous, the elastic constants may be obtained from a knowledge of the natural frequencies in either the axial or radial modes. When to the elasticity a moderate amount of damping is added, quasi-resonances can be set up and the amplitudes at the quasi-nodes measured and compared with the corresponding ones read off Fig. 91 or 92. In the axial case the nodal amplitude can be readily obtained from equation (82), since this expression has minimum values of $2 \sinh \alpha(y-l)$ (providing α is not too large) at the nodes.

When the liquid is merely viscous, the logarithm of the amplitude may be plotted against distance and the approximate value of $\log_{10} \sinh \alpha(y-l)$ used to deduce the value of α. The liquid of large viscosity and small elasticity presents the greatest difficulty to attempts to separate its elastic and viscous constants, since the nodes become ill-defined and are considerably displaced from the positions they would occupy in purely elastic systems. The shortest road to their elucidation in such a case is probably to plot a set of curves such as those of Fig. 91 or 92 for a number of values of α, expressed as multiples of β, and to compare the theoretical and practical distributions of amplitude, noting in particular the values at the best approximations to resonance, i.e. segmental delineation, that one can attain.

Relaxation by Suddenly Applied Shear

An earlier method of studying relaxation, due to Schwedoff,* can be carried out with simple apparatus, though it does not bring out the important effect of the frequency of the applied shear. A simple Couette coaxial-cylinder apparatus (p. 112) is filled with the liquid. The motor intended for rotating the outer cylinder is clamped and the torsion head at the top of the wire supporting the inner cylinder quickly twisted through an angle ϕ. If the liquid is simply viscous, the cylinder will follow until it reaches the same deflection and no twist remains in the wire. If a gel is placed inside, the inner cylinder will only partially take out the twist on the wire through angle θ, leaving a torque remaining on the wire of $c\delta = c(\phi-\theta)$. The rigidity can be measured as

$$N = \frac{c}{4\pi}\left(\frac{b^2-a^2}{a^2b^2}\right)\frac{\delta}{\theta}$$

which is of the same form as (40). In fact, the inner cylinder does not stay in one position with relaxing liquids, but gradually takes out the twist, or most of it. The equation giving the relaxation is

$$S = S_0 e^{it/\tau} \quad \cdots \quad \cdots \quad (85)$$

where S_0 is the value of the strain from which it begins to relax and S is the residual strain at time t. The equation contains τ, which can be calculated from an experimentally obtained curve.

Fig. 96 shows such measurements made by Hatschek and Jane† in a benzo-purpurin gel (3 per cent.). The departure from the exponential curve shows, among other possibilities, that τ varies with S.

Elastic Liquids in Capillary Tubes

Merrington‡ has exemplified the behaviour of these liquids—actually he used rubber solutions—in a remarkable way by forcing them under

---

* *J. de. Physique*, **8**, 341 (1889).   † *Koll. Zeits.*, **39**, 300 (1926).
‡ *Proc. Durham Phil. Soc.*, **10**, 486 (1948).

pressure through capillary tubes.   In entering the tube from a reservoir they are evidently distorted laterally and recover from this by swelling out again on leaving the tube or a little later (Fig. 97, Plate II), depending on the time of relaxation.   From the shape of the recovery section, similar deductions could be made about τ to that which we derived in the last section in equation (85).   Weissenburg* has pointed out that this lateral compression and recovery implies that with this liquid in this type of shear, the viscous forces have components perpendicular to the axis of the tube and not, as with a normal liquid, directed exactly parallel to the direction of flow.

Thixotropy

If a gel is shaken vigorously it will often turn to a sol and reset when the agitation is removed.   Evidently, the structure which confers elasticity has been temporarily broken down.   This gel–sol–gel transformation induced by mechanical vibration was called by Freundlich "thixotropy."

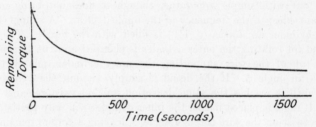

Fig. 96.   Relaxation of benzo-purpurin sol.

Green and Ruth Weltmann† have pointed out that those substances which will respond to movement in this way always show a hysteresis loop in their rate-of-shear : flow curves.   The product of these factors (represented by the area of the loop expressed in the proper units) equals the work done in disrupting the structure.   Most pigment suspensions such as paints and printing inks show thixotropy, but "indifferent" suspensions such as tiny glass spheres in oil do not.   Pryce-Jones‡ has made a special study of this peculiarity and has shown the importance of the time factor in the phenomenon.   He uses a concentric cylinder apparatus, stirring the gel and making measurements of viscosity—as far as possible at comparable rates of shear—at various epochs up to ½ hour after the agitation has ceased.   Using titanium oxide as solid phase and various oils as liquid, he found that the degree of thixotropy, represented by the variation in viscosity with time after agitation, was much affected by the composition of the oil.   Changes as small as 1 per cent. in the free acid content

* *Nature*, **159**, 150 (1947).   † *Ind. Eng. Chem.*, **15**, 20 (1943).
‡ *J. Oil and Colour Chem. Assoc.*, 295 (1936).

of the liquid medium can change a free-flowing paint into a highly thixotropic system, the solid content remaining the same.

This problem is a very important one for the paint and colour manufacturer, who needs a system that is thixotropic, so that it can be stirred and applied as a sol to a surface where it will settle down as a gel and not continue to run. Whether a system of given concentration will act as sol or as gel often depends on the dispersing power of the liquid medium; if this is high, a sol results. In other words, the colloidal environment of the particle plays a big part in the behaviour of these elasto-viscous materials.

ENVOI

At this point I must take leave of those readers who have borne with me so far. It will be apparent that in the last two chapters I have trespassed on ground usually reserved for the rheologists, and in fact to go further in this direction would involve a discussion of the plastic and elastic properties of *solid* bodies. I should like, in conclusion, to commend to the reader two works to which I am myself indebted for inspiration and references, particularly in my first two chapters, i.e. Lamb's *Hydrodynamics* for the classical work and *Modern Developments in Fluid Dynamics* (edited by Goldstein) for the modern aspects. Books on viscometry, such as those of Hatschek, Barr, and Merrington, will also be found to contain much useful information on the instrumental side.

ACKNOWLEDGEMENT

I am greatly indebted to my colleagues W. S. Brown, M.A., R. Roscoe, B.Sc., Ph.D., and H. B. Squire, M.A., for helpful criticism of the manuscript of this book.

INDEX